101

tales from

INDIAN MYTHOLOGY

ANURAG MEHTA

Nita Mehta™
WISKIDZ
ENRICHING YOUNG MINDS

An Imprint of Nita Mehta Publications

Contents

Brahma & Satarupa 4	Saraswati Saves the World........51
Bhishma 6	Jatayu...............52
Vakratunda 8	Bhima & Hidimba 53
The Three Princesses 10	Shurpanakha...........56
Goddess Durga............12	Manu and the Fish 58
Yashoda Ties Krishna...........14	Jatayu Fights Ravana........60
How Sage Agastya was Born?........16	Jatayu Helps Rama..........62
The Birth of Kauravas 18	Krishna Saves Nanda.........63
Rantideva Attains Moksha 20	Kabandha Meets Rama 64
The Story of Sunday 22	Bali & Sugreeva............65
Sage Dadhyan............26	Curse on Bali...........67
Sita's Swayamvara 28	The Mischief of Lord Mars 69
The Great Teacher............30	Birth of Draupadi 70
The Proud Gods............32	The Fruit Vendor 71
Parshurama............35	Krishna Breaks the Bow.......72
Bharata, the Ideal Brother 36	Krishna and Kesi..........73
Mahakaleshwar 37	Tilottama 75
Gajendra 38	Krishna Meets Yama 77
Poison Kills Poison............40	Indra's Fight with Vritra.......79
The Intelligent Beggar 41	Worms in Rice 80
Viradha & Rama............42	Arjuna and Ulupi..........81
Ganesha and Kubera 44	Vishwamitra & Menaka........83
Lord Vishnu's Love for His Devotee...46	The Mountain Bows........85
Maharishi Bhrigu and Vishnu 49	Hanuman Crosses the Sea 87

Krishna Kills Shishupal 89

Ganesha and Ravana 91

Bhima and Kichaka 92

Arjuna's Search 94

Hanuman Meets Sita 96

Ekadanta 98

Hanuman is Captured 99

The Pandavas Save Duryodhana 100

The Parijataka Tree 102

Jaidratha's Punishment 103

Vibhishana Meets Rama 106

Rama & the Squirrel 108

How the Moon Lost its Light? 110

The End of Kumbhakarna 112

Sati 114

The Battle with Meghnad 116

Karna's Promise 118

Krishna's Peace Mission 119

Lakshmana Becomes Unconscious . 121

Bhimeshwar 122

Bhishma Falls 123

The End of Meghnad 124

The Broken Code of War 126

The End of Jaidratha 128

The Fall of Drona 130

Karna Meets His End 132

Gandhari Tries to Protect Her Son ... 134

The True Devotee 136

Ashvatthama's Plan 137

Krishna to the Rescue 138

Sita's Exile 139

Sahasramukharavana 140

Yamaraj Meets Rama 144

Kartikeya 146

Lord Buddha 148

Yama Kumar 149

Brahma Tests Krishna 152

Satyavan and Savitri 154

How Kali was Created? 156

Krishna, the Shepherd Boy 158

Sage Agastya and the Demons 160

Valmiki 162

Krishna Kills Aghasura 164

The Forest Fire 166

The Reformation of Duraasadana ... 168

Krishna Kills the Elephant 170

Indra's Weapon 172

Kedarnath 174

The Demon with Thousand Hands . 176

Luv & Kush Fight Lakshman 178

Curse on Parikshit 180

The Snake Sacrifice 182

Astika Saves Takshaka 184

Brahma & Satarupa

Brahma, the creator of the universe, is depicted with four heads, though originally he had five. While creating the universe, Brahma made a beautiful woman named Satarupa. But Brahma was charmed by his own creation. He had never seen such beauty. Satarupa moved in various directions to avoid the gaze of Brahma.

But Brahma gave himself a second, third, and fourth head, enabling him to see her from all angles. Disgusted, she went skyward and in order to see her, Brahma created a fifth head for himself.

Lord Shiva, the destroyer, was enraged by Brahma's actions. 'Brahma has created Satarupa. She is like his daughter and his duty is to protect her,' he pondered. He felt that it was immoral on Brahma's part to be in love with her and to teach him a lesson, Shiva struck off Brahma's fifth head.

Bhishma

One day, King Shantanu of Hastinapur went hunting. Suddenly, he smelt a sweet fragrance, coming from a beautiful woman named Satyawati. Shantanu fell in love with Satyawati and asked her fisherman father for permission to marry her. The fisherman agreed to this marriage but on the condition that the children born to Satyawati would inherit the throne. This saddened Shantanu as he already had a son, Devavrata. Shantanu returned without Satyawati. Seeing his father heartbroken, Devavrata went to the fisherman.

"I will make sure that Satyawati's son will become king," Devavrata promised the fisherman.

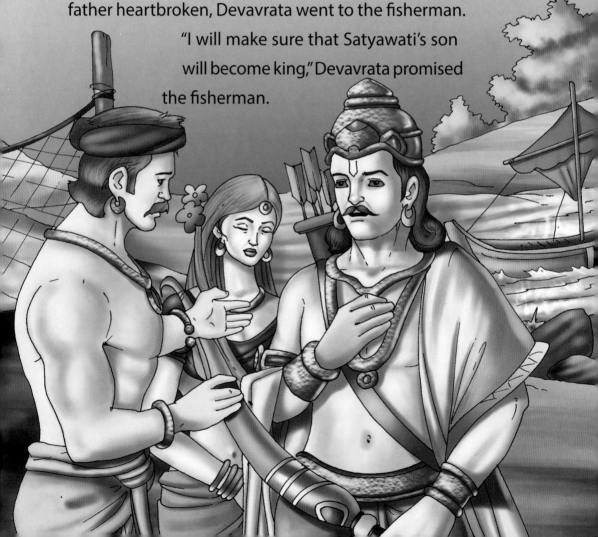

At this the clever fisherman said, "What if your sons try to become king?" To satisfy him Devavrata took a *bhishma pratigya* (strict pledge), never to get married and have children. He then took Satyawati to the palace. Because of this strict promise, he was known as Bhishma.

Vakratunda

Once, Matsar, a demon, asked Sage Shukracharya, "Please tell me how I can rule the worlds?" Shukracharya replied. "You should perform *tapasya* to please Shiva and chant the mantra, *Om Namah Shivaya*."

Matsar stood on one leg for years, chanting the mantra. Pleased, Shiva bestowed a boon on Matsar that no human, God, or demon could kill him. Matsar took over the three worlds—heaven, earth, and patal lok (the underworld). He started troubling everyone. Soon, Matsar conquered Kailash, the home of Shiva. The Gods, including Shiva, prayed to Ganesha because only his Vakratunda (twisted trunk) could defeat Matsar. Finally, taking his Vakratunda form, Ganesha used a weapon that entangled Matsar who then prayed to him for forgiveness. Ganesha said, "I will forgive if you promise to return heaven and earth and never trouble anyone." Matsar promised and Vakratunda set him free.

The Three Princesses

King Shantanu of Hastinapur and his wife Satyawati had two sons, Chitrangada and Vichitravirya. Bhishma, Shantanu's other son, was their guardian. After Shantanu's death Chitrangada was made king, but when he too died, Vichitravirya ascended the throne.

One day, Satyawati asked Bhishma to find brides for Vichitravirya. Bhishma went to Kashi where a *swayamvara* was being held for the three daughters of the king. When the other princes saw Bhishma, they joked that an old man like him had come to marry the young princesses.

Angered, Bhishma forcefully brought the three princesses to Hastinapur. But the first princess, Amba, said that she wanted to marry Prince Shalva and thus the other sisters, Ambika and Ambalika were married to Vichitravirya. One day, Ambika and Ambalika went with their maid to visit the unsightly, Sage Vyasa. Seeing his face, Ambika closed her eyes while Ambalika turned pale. Vyasa cursing them said, "Ambika shall give birth to a blind son and Ambalika will give birth to a pale and weak son." When the maid looked fearlessly at the Sage, he blessed her saying that a very intelligent son would be born to her.

As time passed, Ambika gave birth to Prince Dhritarashtra, who was strong but blind. Ambalika's son Pandu grew to be a great shooter but was weak. Due to his blindness Dhrithrashtra was not crowned the king. Instead Pandu was enthroned. The maid's wise son Vidura was made a minister in the court.

Goddess Durga

Once, a demon called Mahisha, performed severe penances and thus received a boon from Brahma that no man or God would be able to kill him and that he would die only at the hands of a woman. Engulfed with power, he attacked the Gods and captured heaven. The Gods were forced to come down and wander on earth. Angered with their condition, their faces began to glow. The light took the shape of a Goddess, Durga. Each God gave her a weapon while Himalaya gave her a lion. Riding the lion she began to roar. Hearing the roar, Mahisha came out of his palace. Durga killed his army of demons taking many forms, eventually defeating all of them. Finally, Mahisha took the form of a buffalo and attacked her. Durga killed Mahisha with her *trishula*, and since then is worshipped as Goddess Durga.

Yashoda Ties Krishna

One day, finding young Krishna stealing butter from the kitchen, Yashoda quietly crept up from behind and tried to catch him. As he darted away, Yashoda found a long rope to tie him to a tree and chased after him only to realize that it was impossible to catch the quick–footed child. After tiring his mother out, Krishna decided to let her tie him up. Realizing the rope was too small, Yashoda brought some more and tied him to a mortar.

Soon there was a loud noise. Everyone rushed out to see that Krishna had dragged the heavy mortar, and when he got stuck between two trees he had pulled so hard that they had fallen down.

These trees were the cursed sons of Kuber, the God of wealth. By making them fall Krishna had freed them from the curse.

How Sage Agastya was Born?

Once Indra, the king of Gods, commanded Agni (the Fire God) and Vayu (the Wind God) to seek and destroy all the demons. Agni and Vayu killed most of the demons but the rest hid in the ocean. So they returned and told Indra that they could not kill all the demons.

Indra angrily ordered Agni and Vayu, "Even if you have to churn the ocean, you must get those demons out and kill them."

Agni and Vayu said that they didn't want to churn the ocean as there were other creatures living in it and would suffer because of the demons.

Not convinced, Indra said, "The ocean has given shelter to the wicked and should suffer for that. But you two are trying to evade your duty by disobeying me. I curse you to be born as humans on earth." Thereafter, Agni was born as Sage Agastya while Vayu took birth as Sage Vashishtha.

The Birth of Kauravas

Gandhari, the princess of Gandhara kingdom, was chosen as the bride for Dhritarashtra. Dhritarashtra was blind. Not wanting to be better than her husband in any respect, Gandhari tied a silk bandage on her eyes and pledged never to remove it.

Gandhari wanted a hundred children so she prayed to Sage Vyasa who granted her this boon. But she gave birth to a lump of flesh.

Just then the sage Vyasa appeared, and taking the shapeless mass of flesh, he divided it into a hundred and one pieces. One by one, he placed each piece in a jar.

In nine months, in one of the jars, a baby appeared. As soon as he was formed, jackals howled, donkeys brayed, the day became night and a wailing wind rattled the rooftops.

"This child will destroy the world," everyone said, terrified. "Leave him in the forest where the beasts will destroy him."

But Dhritarashtra refused, and brought his son home. The child was named Duryodhana, or the one hard to conquer. A month later, ninety-nine other princes came forth. From the last jar was born Gandhari's only daughter, Dushala. Thus were born Gandhari's hundred sons who were called the Kauravas.

Rantideva Attains Moksha

Once Brahma and the other Gods asked Vishnu, "Who is your most devoted follower?" Vishnu named King Rantideva as his most devout devotee.

Famine had struck Rantideva's kingdom. He had been chanting Vishnu's name while fasting for forty-eight days. He believed Vishnu lived in all human beings. The Gods decided to test Rantideva by seeing if he would share his food after his long fast.

Someone had brought Rantideva some food and just as he began to eat, a Brahmin appeared saying, "Could you give me some food?" Rantideva gave him half his share. The Brahmin blessed him and went away.

In this way, each God changed their form and begged Rantideva for food, and he gladly gave them his share. Yama tested him by appearing as an untouchable who needed water. Rantideva willingly gave him water. The Gods were very happy. Vishnu appeared and blessed Rantideva and granted him *moksha* which means freedom from all worldly troubles.

The Story of Sunday

There was once an old woman who worshipped the Sun God. Every morning, she would clean her house by plastering it with cow dung. Only then would she cook and eat anything.

She used to collect the cow dung from her neighbour's house. Not liking this, the neighbour's wife tied her cow inside the house. The next day, the old woman did not get any cow dung and could not plaster her house. As the house was not clean, she had to fast that day.

That night, the Sun God came in her dream and promised to give her a cow. The next morning she found a cow and a calf in her house. The neighbour's wife saw that the cow produced dung made of gold. Jealous, she greedily replaced the gold dung with ordinary dung.

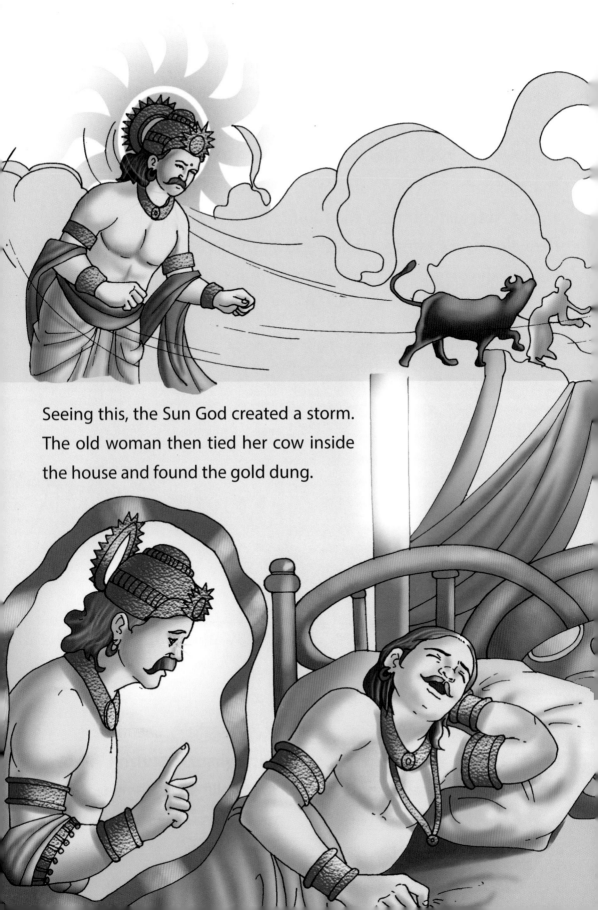

Seeing this, the Sun God created a storm.
The old woman then tied her cow inside
the house and found the gold dung.

The neighbour's wife went to tell the king about the magic cow. The king took away the magic cow and plastered his palace with the gold dung. At night the Sun God appeared in the king's dream and said, "The cow was a gift for the old lady."

The next morning the King awoke to a foul stench only to find the gold dung replaced by ordinary dung. Repenting his actions, he returned the cow to the old lady and punished the neighbour's cunning wife. He also declared that the people of his kingdom should fast on Sundays, the day of the Sun God.

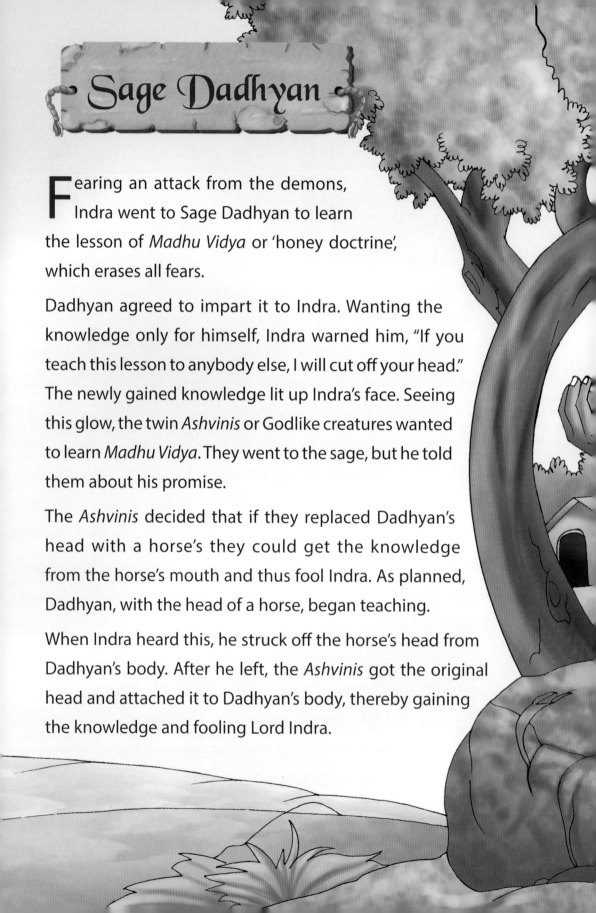

Sage Dadhyan

Fearing an attack from the demons, Indra went to Sage Dadhyan to learn the lesson of *Madhu Vidya* or 'honey doctrine', which erases all fears.

Dadhyan agreed to impart it to Indra. Wanting the knowledge only for himself, Indra warned him, "If you teach this lesson to anybody else, I will cut off your head." The newly gained knowledge lit up Indra's face. Seeing this glow, the twin *Ashvinis* or Godlike creatures wanted to learn *Madhu Vidya*. They went to the sage, but he told them about his promise.

The *Ashvinis* decided that if they replaced Dadhyan's head with a horse's they could get the knowledge from the horse's mouth and thus fool Indra. As planned, Dadhyan, with the head of a horse, began teaching.

When Indra heard this, he struck off the horse's head from Dadhyan's body. After he left, the *Ashvinis* got the original head and attached it to Dadhyan's body, thereby gaining the knowledge and fooling Lord Indra.

Sita's Swayamvara

King Janaka of Mithila had organized a grand *swayamvara* for his beautiful daughter, Sita. *Swayamvara* was the ritual where kings and princes from different lands would visit the king's court asking for the princess's hand, but only the bravest would be selected. King Janaka announced that he had a mighty bow, blessed by Shiva. The one who could string the bow would marry Sita.

Many princes tried in vain but nobody could even lift the bow. Rama and Lakshmana were also present. Everyone stared at Rama as he proceeded towards the bow. Rama, to their amazement bent down and lifting the formidable bow, snapped it into two.

King Janaka proclaimed, "My beloved daughter Sita is to be wedded to Rama." Sita walked up to Rama and garlanded him.

The Great Teacher

One day as the princes of Hastinapur were playing together, their ball fell into a well. Then a ring, too, fell into the well. The princes peered into the well wondering how to retrieve them.

Acharya Drona, standing nearby said, "It is a shame that princes like you are not able to do such a small thing." He picked up a blade of grass and shot it at the ball in the well. The blade got stuck to the ball. Then he shot another blade, which stuck to the end of the first blade. In this way, he made a chain of grass blades, reaching the top of the well.

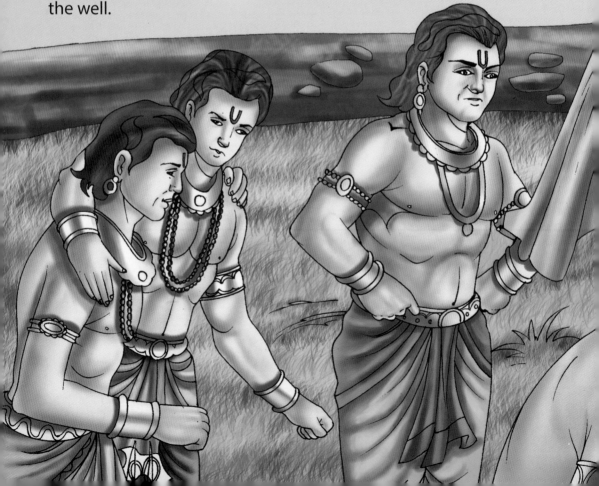

He then pulled out the ball with it. Then he shot an arrow at the ring in the well. The arrow sprung back, and brought the ring with it. The princes were very happy. The princess related the incident to their great grand uncle, Bhishma.

Bhishma felt that Acharya Drona was skilled enough to teach the princes archery and warfare and later made him the princes' teacher.

The Proud Gods

The demons once defeated the Gods and began ruling the world causing a lot of destruction. The Gods went to the all powerful Brahma, the creator of the universe. Blessing them, Brahma told them to fight the demons again. This time the Gods won and got their kingdom back.

Celebrating their victory the Gods began overlooking their duties. They became very proud and forgot their victory was because of Brahma's blessings. Deciding to teach them a lesson, Brahma sent a *yaksha* (demi God) to their kingdom.

When Indra, the king of Gods, saw the *yaksha*, he sent Agni, the Fire God, to him. Agni said, "My powers can burn anything." The *yaksha* gave him a blade of grass and asked him, "Can you burn this?" Agni laughingly said, "Such a small thing, I can burn it in a second." Agni tried to burn the blade but failed. Ashamed, he returned.

Then Indra sent Pawan, the Wind God. Pawan told *yaksha* that his powers could blow away anything. The *yaksha* gave him the same blade of grass and asked, "Can you blow this away?" Pawan placed the blade on his palm and blew at it, but couldn't even move it. He too returned in shame. Indra then went himself and bowing low, asked the *yaksha, his purpose of coming.*

"You Gods have become so proud that you do not recognize that I am Brahma's messenger," said the *yaksha* angrily. I have come to make you realize that it is Brahma who is the most powerful and he made you win. Now leave your pride and fulfil your duties," said the *yaksha* as he left.

The Gods realized their mistake and humbly went about to doing their duties as before.

Parshurama

Parshurama, the sixth avatar of Vishnu, had a violent temper. On hearing about Rama breaking the bow at Sita's *swayamvara*, he became furious. A master archer and a disciple of Shiva, Parshurama could not bear to hear of Rama's triumph. Being a proud Brahmin priest, he disliked the idea of a 'Kshatriya,' a man belonging to the warrior class, emerging victorious. He decided to meet Rama and challenge him. On their way to Ayodhya, Rama and his entourage were rudely interrupted by Parshurama. Wielding his famous axe, Parshurama promptly attacked Rama. Rama, on the other hand, countered it with his *kondanda* bow, and a fierce battle ensued. While the battle continued, their eyes met and everything changed. There was love in place of rage, and respect instead of hatred. Recognizing each other as different forms of the same supreme Vishnu, they threw their weapons and embraced each other.

Bharata, the Ideal Brother

Hearing about Rama's exile, Bharata left for Dandaka forest with an entourage to find Rama. When he saw him, he fell at Rama's feet and begged forgiveness for his mother's behaviour and informed Rama about their father's death. The news greatly saddened Rama, Lakshmana, and Sita. Bharata then pleaded, "I have come on behalf of the people of Ayodhya. Please accept the throne which lies empty without you." Rama answered, "I am only fulfilling our father's wish." Realizing that Rama would not return to Ayodhya, Bharata asked Rama to give his sandals to him. "Step on them so that your presence is forever felt. I shall place them on the throne and serve them faithfully till you return." Rama gave Bharata his sandals and they were placed on the throne till Rama's return.

Mahakaleshwar

Once there was a Brahmin who worshipped Lord Shiva. The wicked demon King Dushan came to Avantika after attaining a boon of invisibility from Lord Brahma and began torturing the Brahmins during their meditation. On being attacked the Brahmins started praying to Lord Shiva. Shiva then appeared in his *Mahakal* form and burnt Dushan to ashes. After this, a *Jyotirlinga* (shrine where Shiva is worshipped) called Mahakaleshwar was set up in Avantika, now known as Ujjain.

Gajendra

Gajendra, the king of elephants lived with his family on a mountain. On a hot summer day as temperatures soared, he and his family descended the mountain to bathe in the cold waters of the lake below. Gajendra playfully began spraying the chilly water with his trunk. As the still waters moved, a crocodile living in that lake got disturbed. Angry, he stealthily attacked Gajendra and sunk his teeth into his leg. Startled, Gajendra cried out in pain.

As his leg bled, he tried to pull it out from the crocodile's jaws. Deeply bruised, his strength failed him. Gajendra anxiously began praying to Vishnu. Before long, the majestic figure of the Lord seated on Garuda emerged. Though crying in pain, Gajendra welcomed Vishnu with a lotus. Vishnu swam out to the crocodile and tore its jaws apart, eventually killing the animal and saving Gajendra.

Poison Kills Poison

Duryodhana, the eldest Kaurava always wanted to be king of Hastinapur. He was constantly looking for ways to harm his cousins, the Pandavas, who had equal rights to the throne. One day, with the help of his uncle Shakuni, he made a devious plan to kill Bhima, the strongest of the Pandavas. He invited Bhima for a picnic near the bank of river Ganga. Duryodhana had poisoned some of the *laddoos* that were served and offered them to Bhima who loved food. As soon as Bhima ate them, he fainted under the effect of the poison and Duryodhana pushed him into the river. In the river many poisonous snakes bit Bhima. It is said that 'poison kills poison.' The poison from the snakes counteracted the effect of the poison from the *laddoos*. Bhima was saved; he swam to the surface and returned home.

The Intelligent Beggar

Two sages lived in an ashram. One day, after their prayers, as they began to eat their food, a beggar came to them. He begged for food but the sages refused saying they had none.

The beggar asked, "O respected saints, may I ask you, who you worship?" They replied, "We worship Pawan, the Wind God, who is also prana (*the breath of life*)." He then asked, "Whom did you offer this food to before eating it yourself?" They said, "We offered it to Pawan or *prana*."

At this, the beggar said, "I hope you know that *prana* is present in all living creatures." The sages replied, "Yes, we know that." The beggar then said, "By denying food to me, you are denying food to *prana* who is present in me and for whom you have prepared it." The sages listened carefully to what the beggar was saying.

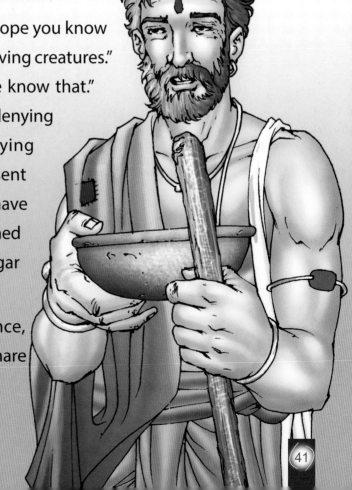

Ashamed at their ignorance, the sages then offered to share their food with the beggar.

Viradha & Rama

As Rama along with Sita and Lakshmana roamed the huge Dandaka forest, they chanced upon a man-eating monster called Viradha.

The monster lifted Sita and was about to abduct her when Rama used his bow. Seeing the puny bow, Viradha laughed and broke it with his finger saying, "You cannot harm me with any weapon for I have a boon which ensures that I cannot be killed."

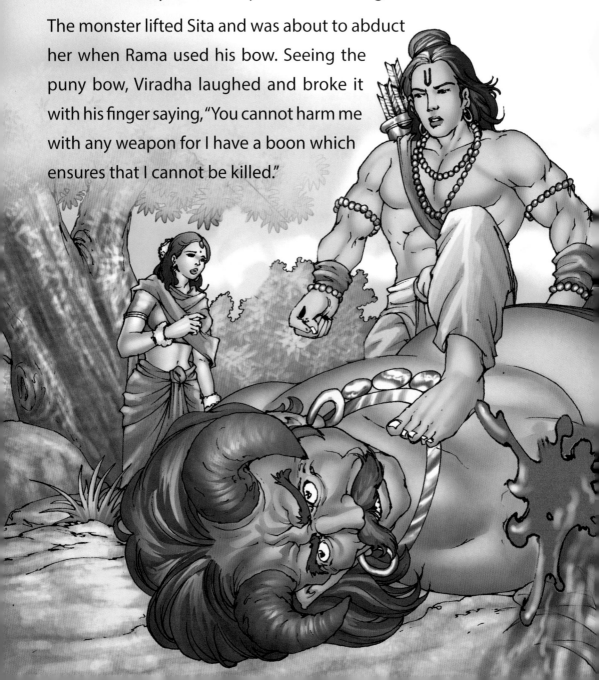

Realizing the futility of using bows, Rama and Lakshmana, with great gusto wrenched off Viradha's arms and threw him on the ground. Rama immediately planted his foot on Viradha. The touch had a wondrous effect. Viradha's eyes softened, and with folded hands he said, "Your touch has purified me. I am a *gandharva* (nature spirit), and not a monster. Please kill me and relieve me of my curse."

Accepting Viradha's request, Rama killed him. The monster's body then changed into a *gandharva* and soared up to the skies.

Ganesha and Kubera

Kubera, the God of wealth was very proud of his fortune. One day he visited Shiva and Parvati in Mount Kailash and invited them for a meal. Shiva and Parvati declined saying, "Ganesha will come instead of us but he eats a lot." Kubera replied, "He can eat as much as he wants." When Ganesha sat down to eat, he ate all the food. But his hunger was not satisfied. So he ate the utensils, the furniture, and the palace. He continued eating and ate Kubera's entire kingdom.

Kubera begged him to stop but Ganesha threatened, "If you don't give me food, I will eat you." Kubera went to Shiva for help, apologizing for his pride. Shiva gave Kubera a handful of rice to give to Ganesha. Kubera went back and offered the rice to Ganesha with love and humility. Ganesha's hunger was finally satisfied and Kubera learned his lesson.

Lord Vishnu's Love for His Devotee

Once, King Ambrish had observed a three day fast to worship Lord Vishnu. Before breaking it, he invited sages and Brahmins for a feast. "I will eat only after taking a bath," said Durvasa, one of the invited sages. It took Durvasa longer than expected to return. As all the guests waited, the Brahmins told Ambrish that if he didn't break his fast before noon, it would be a sin. "If I eat before Durvasa, he will feel insulted," replied Ambrish. The Brahmins then suggested, "Break the fast with water now, and then have food when Durvasa returns. This would save you from both; sinning, and insulting Durvasa."

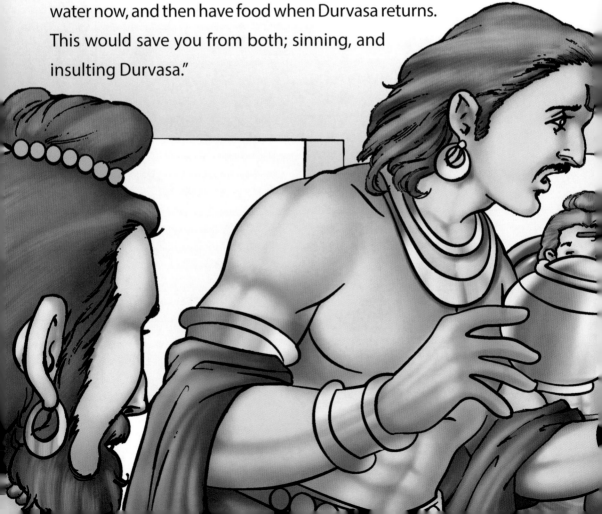

Just as Ambrish was about to drink water, Durvasa returned. He shouted angrily, "How dare you break your fast without me?" Durvasa threw a *chakra* towards Ambrish, who ran to save his life. Ambrish went to Vishnu for help.

Vishnu sent out his *chakra*. It destroyed Durvasa's *chakra* and started chasing him. Terrified, Durvasa ran over hills and valleys, but the *chakra* continued to follow him. He went to Brahma, who could not help him and then to Shiva, who asked him to go to Vishnu. But Vishnu said, "You have insulted my devotee. Only he can forgive you." Durvasa then begged Ambrish for his life. Ambrish thus prayed to Vishnu and the *chakra* immediately disappeared.

Maharishi Bhrigu and Vishnu

Once a debate arose as to whom among Brahma, Shiva, and Vishnu was the greatest. After much thought, it was decided that the noble sage, Bhrigu, would be sent to test the three Gods.

Bhrigu first went to Brahma, but did not pay his respects to him. Brahma felt very insulted at this behaviour.

His next destination was Mount Kailash, where Shiva resided. He told Shiva that he was not happy with his ways. The God, who was known for his violent temper, chased Bhrigu with a trident.

Somehow managing to escape, Bhrigu reached Vaikunthloka where Vishnu was reclining on Sheshnag. Bhrigu kicked Vishnu on his chest. Vishnu woke up as a result of the blow, bowed in reverence and said, "I was not aware of your arrival. Please forgive me. Your feet must be hurting as my chest is very hard. Vishnu then began pressing his feet.

Seeing Vishnu's reaction, Bhrigu concluded that Lord Vishnu was the greatest among the trinity.

Saraswati Saves the World

Once Shiva was woken from his meditation and saw the world filled with evil. Shiva decided it was time to wipe the slate clean. He opened his world destroying third eye which created a terrible fire that threatened all existence. Saraswati took the form of a river and absorbed the fire. She took it into the sea where it formed a fire breathing creature called Badavagni. Saraswati declared, "As long as man is wise, this animal will remain here, but if man becomes corrupt, this beast will destroy the world."

Jatayu

Approaching Panchvati, Rama, Lakshmana, and Sita encountered a huge vulture swooping down towards them. Rama confronted him asking. "Who are you?" The bird saluted them and said, "I am Jatayu, King Dasharatha's friend." Jatayu told them that he had protected Dasharatha during the battle with Samparasura. Rama welcomed his father's saviour.

Jatayu then mentioned that he was the grandson of Sage Kashyap and his father Arun, was the charioteer of the Sun God, Surya. He also narrated how his elder brother Sampati had burnt his wings while trying to save him from soaring towards the sun. Jatayu had come to the forest of Panchavati where he was entrusted with the kingship of vultures. Jatayu then promised Rama to protect them with all his might.

Bhima & Hidimba

Once, while the Pandavas were walking for a long time, they came to the part of the forest where a demon named Hidimb and his sister Hidimba lived.

Tired, Kunti and the four Pandavas fell asleep while Bhima stayed awake and kept watch. Sensing the smell of humans, Hidimb asked Hidimba to search for them. As soon as Hidimba saw the handsome Bhima, she fell in love.

Assuming the form of a beautiful woman, she said, "I am Hidimba, my brother is a demon, he will eat all of you." Bhima smiled and replied, "Don't worry, I am strong enough to defeat your brother."

When Hidimba did not return, Hidimb went looking for her and saw her talking to Bhima. He shouted furiously, "I sent you to kill the human and you are talking to him. I will kill him myself." Saying so, he attacked Bhima. A fierce fight ensued and ended with Bhima killing Hidimb. The thunderous roars of the two fighters woke Kunti and the four Pandavas. Hidimba told them that she was a demoness but wished to marry Bhima. With Kunti's permission the marriage took place and soon Hidimba gave birth to a son named Ghatotkacha.

As time passed, Kunti and the Pandavas decided to leave the forest. They took leave of Hidimba and Ghatotkacha, who had grown up to be a strong boy. Ghatotkacha promised the Pandavas that he would come to them, whenever they needed him.

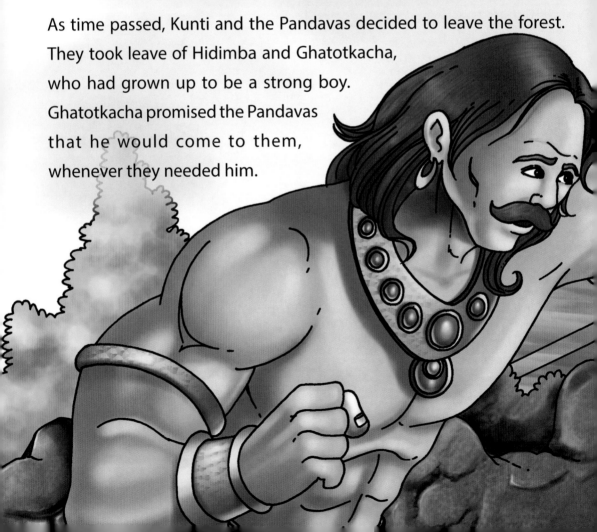

Shurpanakha

At the end of their exiled period, Rama, Lakshmana, and Sita stayed in Panchavati. One day as Rama sat chanting his scriptures, a female demon named Shurpanakha happened to see him and was enchanted by him. She fell in love with Rama.

Shurpanakha was very ugly and in order to attract Rama, she transformed herself into a beautiful maiden and approached him saying, "I am Shurpanakha, sister of Ravana, demon-king of Lanka. I want to be your wife." He refused saying that he was already married.

Shurpanakha then spotted Lakshmana and similar feelings were aroused seeing the equally handsome brother. She asked Lakshmana, who also rejected her offer.

Unable to bear this insult, Shurpanakha turned back to her original form of a demoness and attacked Sita. This angered Lakshmana and he took a sword and cut off Shurpanakha's nose.

Manu and the Fish

One day as King Manu collected water from a river, a small fish swam into his vessel. As he tried to throw it back, the small fish begged, "Please save me from the big fish." Pitying the fish, the king kept it in a bowl of water. By the next morning, the fish had grown big so Manu put it in a tank. Day after day, the fish kept growing in size and finally it was so big that it had to be taken to the ocean. As Manu was putting the fish in the ocean, the fish said, "I am Matsya, the avatar of Vishnu.

In a few days, a big flood will submerge the whole earth. You must build a big ship and fill it with people, animals and plants of all kind."

As the fish had predicted, it rained continuously for seven days and seven nights and all the creatures drowned in the flood except those who were on Manu's ship. Manu created a new kingdom on earth with the creatures who had survived.

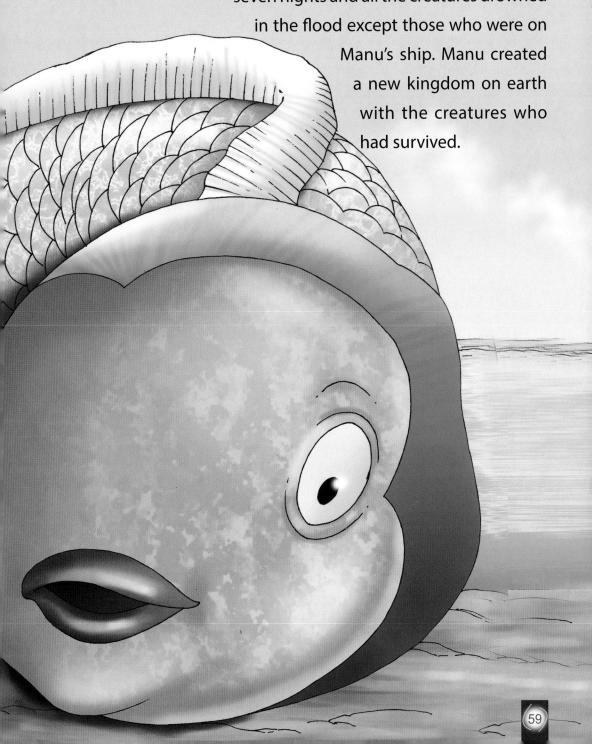

Jatayu Fights Ravana

When Ravana was taking Sita away to Lanka in his flying chariot, Jatayu, the wise old bird, was resting in the forest. Hearing Sita's helpless screams, Jatayu flew to Ravana's chariot.

Being a great devotee of Rama, Jatayu could not remain quiet at the plight of Sita even though he knew that he was no match for the mighty Ravana. Nevertheless, he challenged Ravana's strength, fully aware that he would get killed by obstructing Ravana's path. Jatayu decided to save Sita from the clutches of Ravana at any cost.

He stopped Ravana and ordered him to leave Sita, but Ravana threatened to kill him if he interfered. Chanting Rama's name, Jatayu attacked Ravana with his sharp claws and hooked beak.

His sharp nails and beak tore Ravana's flesh. Ravana took out his diamond–studded arrow and fired at Jatyayu's wings. As the arrow hit, one frail wing tore off and fell, but the brave bird continued fighting. With his other wing, he bruised Ravana's face and tried to pull Sita from the chariot. The fight continued till Jatayu was bleeding from the wounds all over his body.

Finally, Ravana took out his sword and struck Jatayu's other wing. As it hit, the bird fell on the ground, bruised and battered.

Jatayu Helps Rama

Discovering the deceit by the demon Mareecha, Rama grew anxious about Sita and Lakshmana whom he had left alone in the forest. Running through the dense forest, he called out their names. Soon, he saw Lakshmana, and told him about Mareecha's deceit; how, by imitating Rama's voice, he made Lakshmana leave Sita in search for Rama. Anxious that something terrible might have happened to Sita, the brothers rushed home. On reaching, they found the door ajar with the fruits scattered. Sita was nowhere in sight. As they anxiously searched through the forests, they chanced upon the injured bird, Jatayu. Writhing in pain, the bird just managed to tell them about Sita's abduction and pointed to the direction in which Ravana had gone. With folded wings, he bid farewell and breathed his last.

Krishna Saves Nanda

O ne day, Nanda Maharaja, Krishna's father, went to take a dip in the Yamuna at an unfavourable time. Seeing Nanda in the river at such an odd hour, the attendants of Varuna, the sea God, arrested him and took him to their master.

When Nanda Maharaja was taken away, Nanda's companions went to Krishna for help, who immediately left for Varuna's adobe. Elated to see Krishna, Varuna, a devotee of Lord Krishna immediately released Nanda and begged him for forgiveness.

Kabandha Meets Rama

While searching for Sita, Rama and Lakshmana saw a ferocious demon in the forest named Kabandha.

The hungry demon caught hold of them and was about to devour them, when the brothers fired arrows and cut off his arms. As Kabandha lay bleeding he asked, "Who are you." When Rama and Lakshmana introduced themselves, Kabandha bowed in reverence and told them his story. "Brahma had cursed me to change into a demon for my misdeeds and only if Rama would kill me would I get back to my earlier form." Kabandha then begged Rama to end his life. As his body burnt to ashes a beautiful figure emerged from it. After changing into a *gandharva*, Kabandha advised Rama to seek Sugreeva's help and recover Sita.

Bali & Sugreeva

The son of Indra, Bali, was the monkey king of Kishkindha. His younger brother was Sugreeva. The kingdom had a sworn enemy called Manyavi. Tired of the demon's attack, Bali decided to settle the score. When Bali and Manyavi entered a cave during their fight, Sugreeva was ordered to keep a watch outside till Bali emerged victorious.

Time passed and sounds of the roaring fight wafted to Sugreeva's ears. After nearly a year's wait when neither Bali nor the demon came out, Sugreeva assumed both were dead. Saddened by his brother's death, he went back to Kishkindha and became its ruler and made Tara, Bali's wife, his queen. However, Bali returned and seeing Sugreeva as king, felt betrayed. Though Sugreeva tried to explain the misunderstanding, Bali attacked him, forcing him and his team of monkeys to flee Kishkindha. Bali regained his kingship but became Sugreeva's enemy forever.

Curse on Bali

Bali had killed a demon named Dundubhi. Sugreeva showed Rama the demon's carcass and told Rama the reason about making Rishyamooka his hiding spot.

He informed Rama that the famous Sage Matanga lived in the Rishyamooka mountains. When Bali had swung the battered body of Dundubhi from Kishkindha, it fell inside the Sage's ashram.

The sage had become enraged because he had built the ashram after years of worship and organized *yagnas* there. Sage Matanga roared, "Who dares to tarnish my ashram with a blood–smeared corpse?" When no answer came, he sat down in deep meditation and discovered Bali's name. In a fury, the sage cursed Bali and his men to be destroyed if they ever entered the forests of Rishyamooka.

Sugreeva thus added that because Bali would hunt him down wherever he went, he took shelter in these forests knowing that Bali could not enter it.

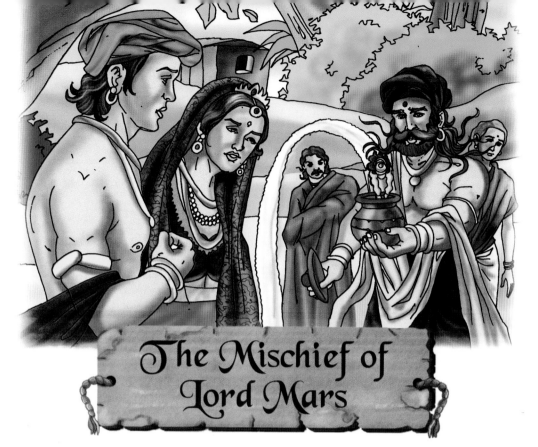

The Mischief of Lord Mars

Once, a couple was travelling through a forest. When Mars saw the beautiful woman he felt like creating some mischief. Taking the form of the husband, he went to the couple. He asked the wife to go with him. The real husband became angry and they started fighting. Some villagers came to see what was going on, but nobody, including the wife, could tell who the real husband was.

One of the villagers realized that some heavenly spirit had taken the form of the husband. He brought an earthen pot with a spout and said, "Whoever can enter this pot through this spout is the real husband." At this the real husband said that it was an unfair test, he could never enter the pot. But Mars knew how to change the shape of his body. He made his body small and entered the pot through the spout. The villager closed the pot and Mars was trapped in it. The husband and his wife continued with their journey.

Birth of Draupadi

King Drupada and Acharya Drona were enemies. One day, Drupada asked two sages, Yaja and Upayaja, to perform a *yagna* that could give Drupada a son who could kill Drona. When the *yagna* was over, the sages offered the *prasada* to Drupada's wife. At that moment, the queen had something in her mouth so she asked the sages to wait. Angered, Yaja put the *prasada* in the *yagna* fire. Suddenly from the fire emerged a young warrior. Similarly Upayaja also put the *prasada* in the fire from which emerged a beautiful woman. A voice was heard from the sky, "This woman has taken birth to become the cause of destruction of those who are evil." The woman came to be known as Draupadi after her father Drupada and the warrior was called Dhrishtadyumna.

The Fruit Vendor

One day, young Krishna heard a fruit vendor call out, "Who will buy my fresh fruits?"

Seeing the cart full of ripe fruits he ran inside to get grains. Now, in those days all goods used to be bought not with money, but by bartering or exchanging with other items, and Krishna had seen his parents doing that.

Barely managing to hold the grains in his tiny hands Krishna offered him whatever he could. The vendor liked the innocence of the child. He accepted the grains and lovingly filled the child's hands with fruits in return. As he turned to leave he found his cart full of precious jewels instead of fruits.

He immediately understood that God had showered blessings for his kindness.

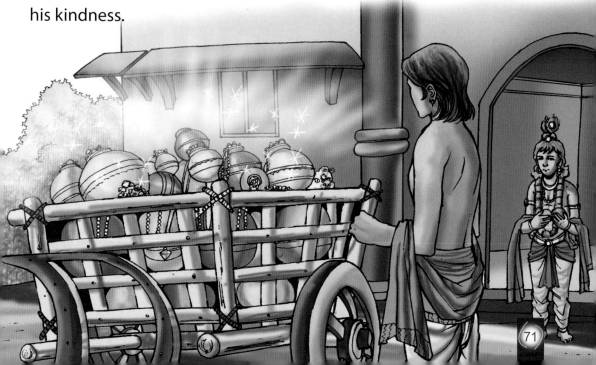

Krishna Breaks the Bow

Krishna and Balaram arrived at the venue where Kansa's famous sacrifice, the *Dhanur yagna*, was to be held. There, an enormous bow was placed on a platform to display Kansa's power.

Seeing the bow, Krishna went ahead to pick it up but was stopped by the guards. A fight followed and the guards were thrashed. Krishna then climbed on the platform, held the heavy bow in his hand and strung it. The bow broke with a thunderous sound, so loud that it even reached Kansa's ears, miles away in his chamber.

The sound was like a clear signal to Kansa that the eighth child of his sister Devaki had finally arrived and that his end was near. In desperation, Kansa sent an army of men to capture Krishna but was defeated after a severe battle.

Krishna and Kesi

Kansa, Krishna's uncle made continuous attempts to kill Krishna. Once he sent the demon Kesi, to kill him. Kesi taking the form of a terrible horse, came galloping to Vrindavan with his mane flowing and hooves clattering.

After entering Vrindavan, Kesi challenged Krishna to a duel which Krishna accepted. Digging up the earth with his hooves, Kesi charged towards Krishna like an angry lion. With great might, he jumped on Krishna and tried to trample him with his hooves.

Krishna caught hold of his legs, swung him around and hurled him on the ground. Kesi fell with a thud and became unconscious. Regaining his senses Kesi again attacked, but this time Krishna put his hands into his mouth and choked him to death.

Tilottama

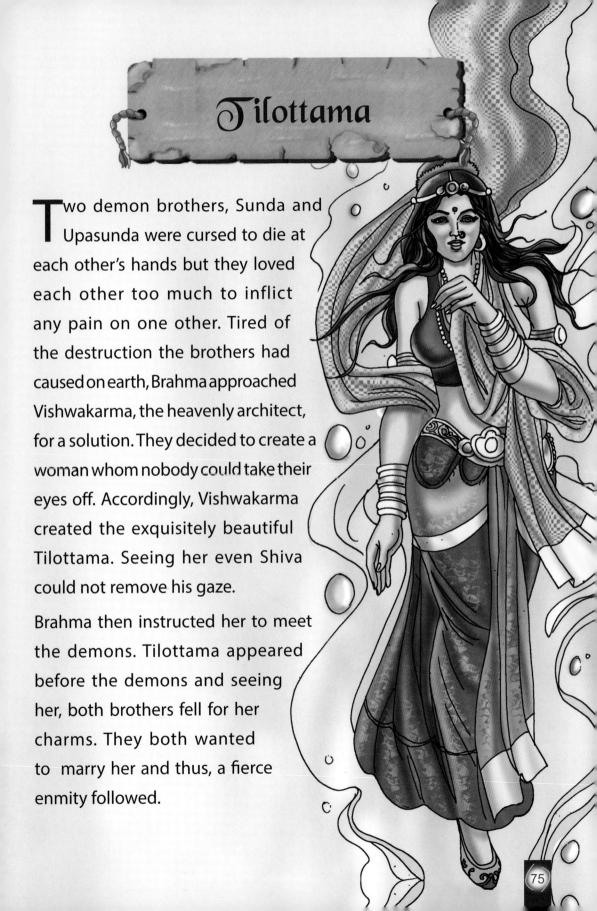

Two demon brothers, Sunda and Upasunda were cursed to die at each other's hands but they loved each other too much to inflict any pain on one other. Tired of the destruction the brothers had caused on earth, Brahma approached Vishwakarma, the heavenly architect, for a solution. They decided to create a woman whom nobody could take their eyes off. Accordingly, Vishwakarma created the exquisitely beautiful Tilottama. Seeing her even Shiva could not remove his gaze.

Brahma then instructed her to meet the demons. Tilottama appeared before the demons and seeing her, both brothers fell for her charms. They both wanted to marry her and thus, a fierce enmity followed.

They took up arms against each other and died fighting. Unfortunately, Tilottama's charms kept captivating one and all. So Brahma cursed her, "Nobody will be able to cast his eyes on you for too long."

Krishna Meets Yama

Krishna and Balaram were trained under Sandipani Muni. On completion of their training, it was time to ask for *gurudakshina*, the offering made to the teacher. Sandipani Muni wanted to ask for something extraordinary so he consulted his wife.

"As my *gurudakshina*, I ask for the return of my drowned son," said Sandipani Muni to the boys. Krishna and Balaram immediately set out for the sea. On reaching its shores, they enquired about the dead son.

The Sea God emerged and told them how Panchajana, a demon, had devoured the child. On hearing this, Krishna plunged into the water and killed Panchajana. He tore open the belly of the demon and found the body of the child.

Krishna then dragged the child's body to Samyamani, the residence of Yama. Happy to receive Krishna, Yama brought the child alive. Sandipani Muni saw the true power of Krishna and blessed him.

Indra's Fight with Vritra

One of Indra's famous battles was with the demon Vritra who took the form of a fearful monster and stole all the water in the world. As the water disappeared, life on earth became threatened. Only Indra could save the world from this disaster.

On hearing what had happened, Indra went charging like thunder towards Vritra's fortress. As the building came crashing down, Indra saw Vritra standing in a corner. They clashed, and after a long drawn out battle, Indra was victorious. He tore open the demon's body from which once again, all the water flowed out. Thus, Indra was hailed as the king of the world.

Worms in Rice

There once lived a great saint named Vedanta Deshikar. Being a simple man, he did not care for wealth and comfort. He was extremely religious and devoted himself completely to God. Everybody praised him for his simplicity and virtuosities.

Each day, Deshikar went from door to door and begged for alms and food. In the same town that Deshikar lived, there was a man who respected him a lot and wanted to gift him something expensive. But he knew very well that the sage would not accept anything.

One day, when the sage came begging at the man's door, he put a few gold coins in the rice that he put in Deshikar's begging bowl. Deshikar went home with the rice but when he saw the gold coins he told his wife, "There are worms in the rice." He carefully separated the rice from the coins. He threw them away and then ate the rice.

Arjuna and Ulupi

After Arjuna had broken a promise, he was exiled for twelve years. While he was in the forest, a beautiful woman called Ulupi saw him and fell in love with him. She was actually a snake and was the daughter of the king of snakes, Kauravya. They lived in the snake kingdom in *patal lok* (netherworld).

One day, when Arjuna went to bathe in the river, Ulupi taking her snake form caught hold of his leg and dragged him to *patal lok*. There, she took him to her palace and asked Arjuna to marry her. Arjuna agreed. They got married and had a son named Iravan. Later, Arjuna wanted to go back to earth and Ulupi took him there. She also gave him a boon that no creature of water could defeat him.

Vishwamitra & Menaka

Once, Sage Vishwamitra was performing a very difficult *tapasya*. Indra, the king of Gods, was afraid that once completed, Vishwamitra would be more powerful and could even conquer heaven. Indra thus sent Menaka, a beautiful dancer of his court, to earth.

Meanwhile, Vishwamitra had performed all the rituals and was engaged in meditation, to complete his *tapasya*.

Menaka went to the forest where Vishwamitra sat with his eyes closed. She sang, danced, made garlands of fragrant flowers and put them around Vishwamitra's neck to attract his attention. All this disturbed Vishwamitra and he opened is eyes. His meditation was broken. Seeing Menaka's beauty, he wished to marry her. They got married and had a daughter. Once Menaka's purpose on the earth was over, she went back to heaven, leaving behind a sad Vishwamitra.

The Mountain Bows

There were two mountains, Vindhya and Meru. The sun used to go around Meru but not Vindhya. This made Vindhya jealous. He asked the sun to encircle him but was refused. In anger, Vindhya steadily started rising towards the heavens, threatening to block the sun's passage from the northern to southern hemisphere.

The sages and Gods were distressed and approached Sage Agastya for help. Agastya went and stood before Vindhya. The mountain, seeing the great sage, bowed down low to show his respect. Agastya blessed him saying, "May you ever remain like this." From that time, the mountain has remained at that height itself. Now the sun's rays reached the earth and all was well again.

Hanuman Crosses the Sea

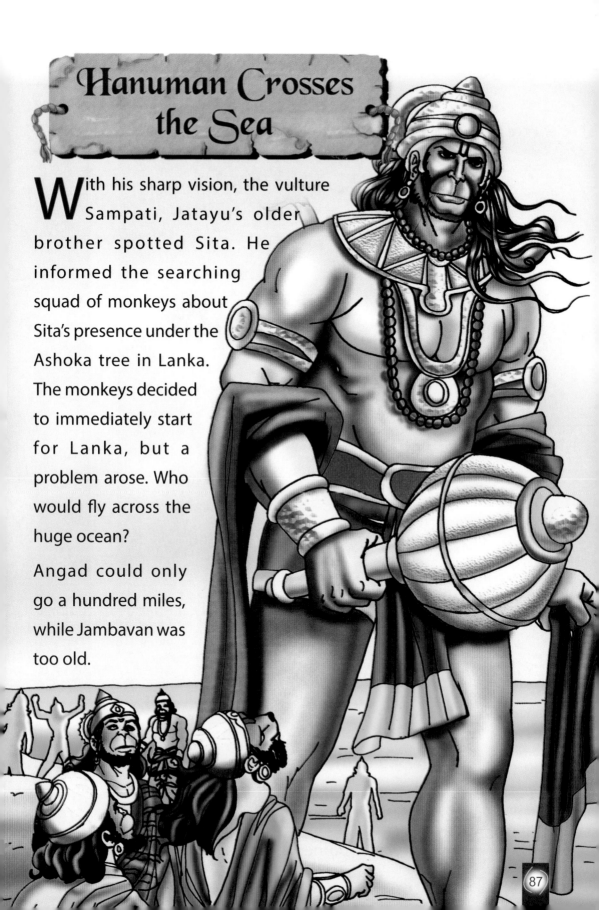

With his sharp vision, the vulture Sampati, Jatayu's older brother spotted Sita. He informed the searching squad of monkeys about Sita's presence under the Ashoka tree in Lanka. The monkeys decided to immediately start for Lanka, but a problem arose. Who would fly across the huge ocean?

Angad could only go a hundred miles, while Jambavan was too old.

Finally, Jamabavan realized that only Hanuman, the son of Vayu, had the capacity to fly across the ocean.

The monkeys reminded Hanuman of his strengths. Inspired by their words, Hanuman offered his prayers and set off on the journey. He assumed his full, gigantic form and with a great roar, leapt up to the skies. With one jump, he reached the peak of a mountain. Within a minute, he was airborne, on his way to find Sita in Lanka.

Krishna Kills Shishupal

Seething with anger at Rukmini's marriage to Krishna, Shishupal, Rukmini's fiancé, wanted revenge. He approached Rukmini's brother Rukmi for his support. But Rukmi refused to help him after his humiliating defeat by Krishna and Balaram.

After Bhima had killed Jarasandha, Yudhishthira organized a famous *Rajsuya yagna* where he invited many kings and princes. Shishupal too was invited. As the *yagna* began, Shishupal saw Krishna in the crowd and began hurling abuses at him.

By insulting Krishna, Shishupal thought he would get the sympathy of the other guests.

The guests stood startled but Krishna remained quiet.

"If you abuse me more than one hundred times, I shall not forgive you," Krishna warned Shishupal. But when Shishupal uttered his hundredth abuse, Krishna turned to him and taking his *Sudarshan Chakra*, flung it at Shishupal. The weapon slashed Shishupal's head. As Shishupal lay dead, the crowds cheered.

Ganesha and Ravana

Ravana was a devout devotee of Shiva. Pleased with his worship, Shiva gave him his *atma linga*. "If the *linga* is ever placed on the ground it will lose its power," Shiva warned Ravana while giving him the *linga*. Alarmed, the Gods begged Shiva to take the *linga* back as that would make the demon Ravana even more powerful. But Shiva declined. The Gods asked Ganesha for help. Changing himself into a cowherd, Ganesha appeared before Ravana, who was then pondering how to take a bath with the *linga* in hand. He asked the boy to hold it for a while. As soon as Ravana turned his back, Ganesha dropped the *linga* saying it was too heavy. Furious, Ravana tried to lift it but failed as the *linga* turned into a cow head. The Gods then breathed a sigh of relief.

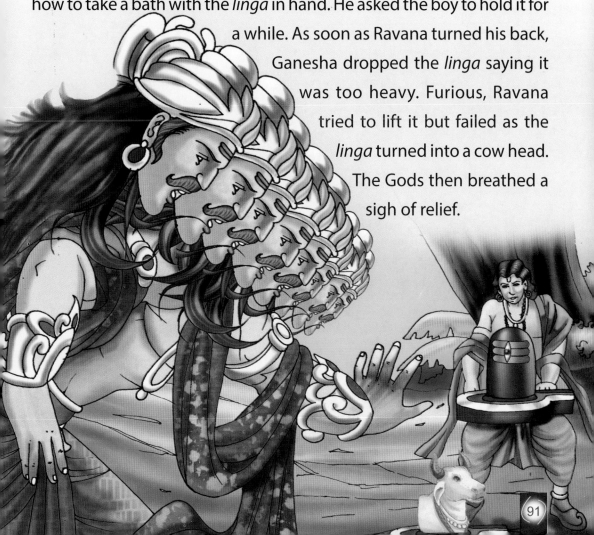

Bhima and Kichaka

The Pandavas along with Draupadi were serving as help in the palace of Viratnagar, disguising their true identities; fulfilling the condition of the bet they had lost to Duryodhana. Draupadi was living in Viratnagar as the Queen's maid. Kichaka was the Queen's brother and the general of the Viratnagar army.

King Virata was weak, so all the powers were in the hands of Kichaka. One day, Kichaka saw Draupadi and fell in love with her, and seeing she was one of the Queen's maids, offered to marry her. Draupadi warned, "Do not trouble me." Angered by her boldness, Kichaka dragged her to the king's court. He kicked and insulted her.

Crying bitterly, Draupadi came to Bhima, who was working as the royal cook and asked him to kill Kichaka.

In the darkness of the night, Kichaka approached an apparently sleeping Draupadi and grasped the covered figure from the back. But to his dismay, the blanket fell off and it was revealed that the unknown person was none other than Bhima! Bhima jumped up and threw Kichaka to the ground. Kichaka fought back valiantly but soon Bhima overpowered him and killed him. The news of the death of Kichaka, who was a great warrior, spread like fire. Eventually, Duryodhana came to know about it and realized that the Pandavas who were thought to be in hiding were in Viratnagar.

Arjuna's Search

During the Pandavas' exile, Sage Vyasa told them, "After your exile, you will have a war with the Kauravas. Arjuna should pray to Lord Shiva for divine weapons." Arjuna went to Mount Kailash and started his penance. Pleased, Shiva disguised himself as a hunter and came to test Arjuna. Just then, a demon, Mooka, attacked Arjuna in the form of a wild boar.

Arjuna shot an arrow and killed it. But he saw another arrow in the body of the boar. He said, "Who dare shoot my prey?"

Shiva, in the hunter's form, said, "I shot the arrow. This is my prey." A long fight ensued between the two and Arjuna grew tired. "I will fight after my prayers," said Arjuna. Arjuna made a Shivalinga and put a garland around it. But suddenly found the garland around the hunter's neck. He understood that the hunter was Shiva. Shiva assumed his real form and bestowed upon him the *pashupatastra*.

Hanuman Meets Sita

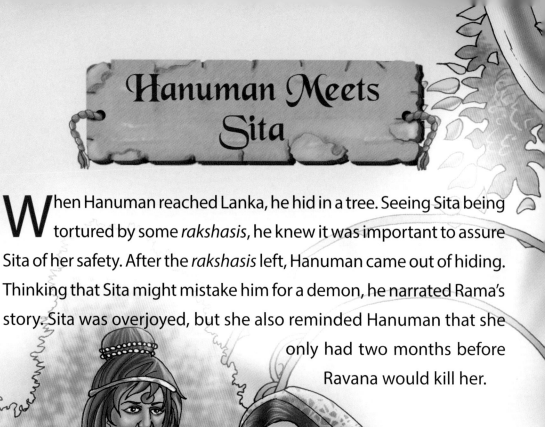

When Hanuman reached Lanka, he hid in a tree. Seeing Sita being tortured by some *rakshasis*, he knew it was important to assure Sita of her safety. After the *rakshasis* left, Hanuman came out of hiding. Thinking that Sita might mistake him for a demon, he narrated Rama's story. Sita was overjoyed, but she also reminded Hanuman that she only had two months before Ravana would kill her.

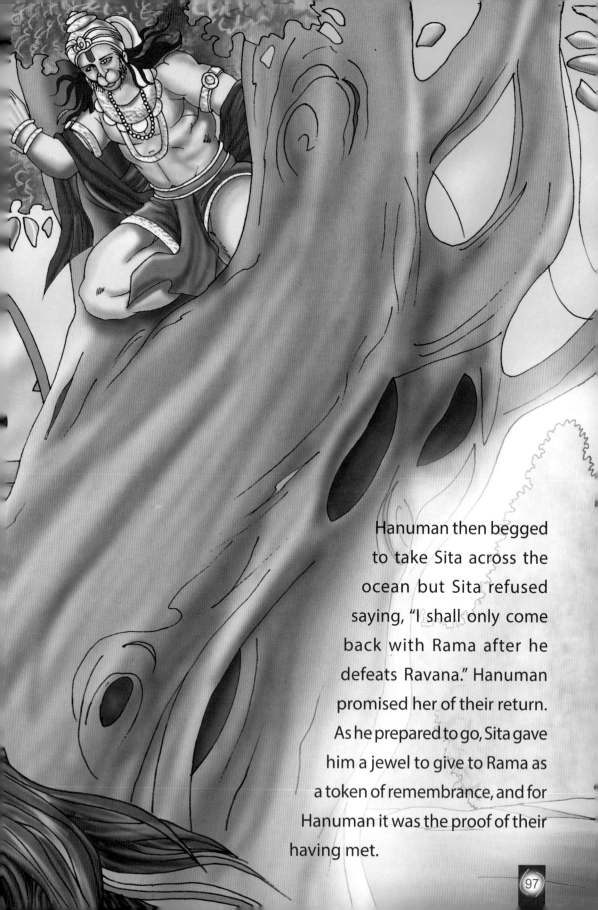

Hanuman then begged to take Sita across the ocean but Sita refused saying, "I shall only come back with Rama after he defeats Ravana." Hanuman promised her of their return. As he prepared to go, Sita gave him a jewel to give to Rama as a token of remembrance, and for Hanuman it was the proof of their having met.

Ekadanta

Once, Parashurama, an *avtaar* of Lord Vishnu visited Mount Kailash, the home of Shiva. As Shiva was asleep, his son Ganesha stopped Parashurama from waking his father. Feeling insulted, Parashurama angrily struck Ganesha with the axe that Shiva had given him. Ganesha recognized his father's axe and received it with respect. The axe cut one of his tusks. Since then, Ganesha is called *Ekadanta*, which means one–toothed.

Hanuman is Captured

Meghnad, Ravana's son, had mastered the art of warfare from Brahma. As Hanuman was leaving Lanka, he created havoc in the city. Hearing about the destruction that Hanuman had inflicted, Meghnad took his father's blessing and set out to kill him.

Hanuman crushed all the arrows that Meghnad shot. Finally, Meghnad decided to use *brahmaastra*, which when shot immobilized Hanuman. But Hanuman was unperturbed, as Brahma had given him a boon that the *brahmaastra* could bind him only for some time. Enraged, *rakshasis* charged at him without knowing that the *brahmaastra* would lose its power on being touched. So, just as the *rakshasis* touched him, Hanuman started reviving. Meghnad, then quickly tied Hanuman and dragged him to Ravana's court where he would receive his punishment.

The Pandavas Save Duryodhana

Duryodhana had come to the forest where the Pandavas were spending their years in exile. There, Chitrasena, the king of the Gandharvas imprisoned him. On hearing this, Yudhisthira said to Arjuna, "We can settle scores with Duryodhana later. An outsider has captured our cousin. It is a question of our clan's honour. Go and rescue him."

Arjuna defeated Chitrasena's soldiers and Chitrasena was forced to descend from heaven. He was Arjuna's friend.

He told Arjuna, "Indra had ordered me to punish Duryodhana and his friends for ridiculing you." Arjuna took Chitrasena to Yudhisthira. "We thank you for your concern for us. But please release Duryodhana now," said Yudhisthira. Chitrasena agreed and released him. Duryodhana felt very humiliated because his most hated enemies, the Pandavas, had saved his life.

The Parijataka Tree

During the churning of the ocean, the Gods had obtained Parijataka, the tree with divine fragrance. This tree was planted in the garden of Indra, the king of Gods. One day Sage Narada went to this garden and collected some flowers that had fallen from the tree and gave them to Rukmini, Krishna's wife. Rukmini was elated but when Satyabhama, Krishna's other wife, smelled its fragrance, she asked Krishna to bring her the tree. After defeating Indra, Krishna brought the tree on earth. But, a quarrel started between Rukmini and Satyabhama, as both wanted the tree. Krishna planted the tree in Satyabhama's courtyard in such a way that its flowers fell in Rukmini's house and thus both his wives were happy.

Jaidratha's Punishment

While they were exiled, one day the Pandavas had gone hunting and their wife, Draupadi was alone in their hut. Jaidratha, the king of Sindhudesha passed by the hut and saw Draupadi. Fascinated by Draupadi's beauty, he approached her and introduced himself. Draupadi remembered he was the husband of Dushala, Duryodhana's sister. Seeing he was a relative, she invited Jaidratha into the hut. "You are so beautiful. Why are you undergoing the hardships of exile with the Pandavas? Come with me, I will make you my queen," urged Jaidratha.

Draupadi felt very insulted on hearing this. "How dare you say that to me? The Pandavas will kill you," she replied. "I am not afraid of them. They are no more than beggars now," said Jaidratha and forced Draupadi into his chariot, taking her away.

Soon the Pandavas returned to their hut and found Draupadi missing. Bhima was very angry as the honour of the Pandavas was at stake. He took his chariot and followed Jaidratha. He captured Jaidratha and dragged him by his hair to Yudhisthira.

Draupadi was crying bitterly. Seeing this, Bhima asked his elder brother's permission to kill Jaidratha. Yudhisthira said, "Jaidratha is our sister's husband. If we kill him, our sister would be widowed. Let us punish him suitably but spare his life."

"By insulting me, he has dishonoured you all. Shave his head but leave five tufts of hair on it. This will be a fitting insult for dishonouring the Pandavas," exclaimed Draupadi. Thus Jaidratha was punished.

Ravana expelled his younger brother Vibhishana from Lanka when he discouraged Ravana from fighting with Rama. Vibhishana decided to seek Rama and help him.

Seeing Vibhishana approach, Sugreeva, the monkey king and the others grew suspicious, but Hanuman assured them of his honest nature. Like a loyal servant, Vibhishana told Rama about Ravana's strengths and weaknesses and also about the boon of immortality granted to Ravana by Brahma.

He gave Rama all the details of Ravana's weapons, soldiers, army, and methods of warfare, including Meghnad's gift of invisibility while fighting his enemy.

This valuable information helped Rama organize his army and fight Ravana. Finally, Vibhishana suggested that Rama should pray to the ocean to help him build the bridge to Lanka and cross the ocean.

Rama warmly hugged Vibhishana and thanked him for all his help promising him protection and the crown of Lanka after defeating Ravana and freeing Sita from his clutches.

Rama & the Squirrel

In order to save Sita from Ravana's clutches, Rama needed to cross the sea to reach Lanka. He began praying to the Sea God. The Sea God arose from the depths of the sea and told Rama to build a bridge across the sea. Rama's entire monkey army began building the bridge by placing boulders.

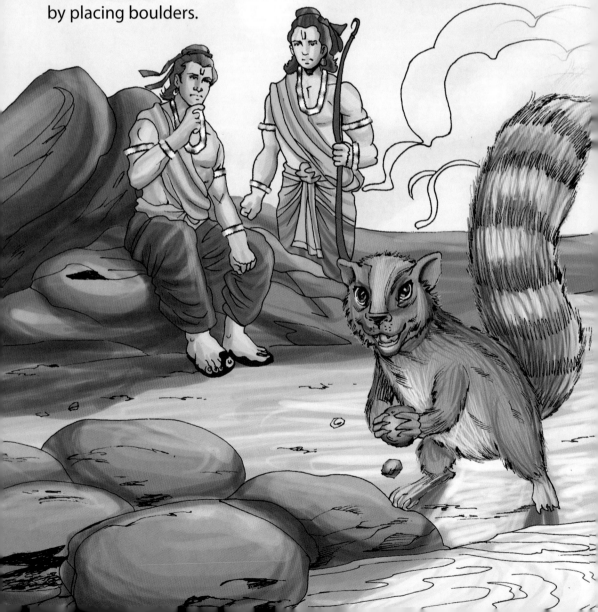

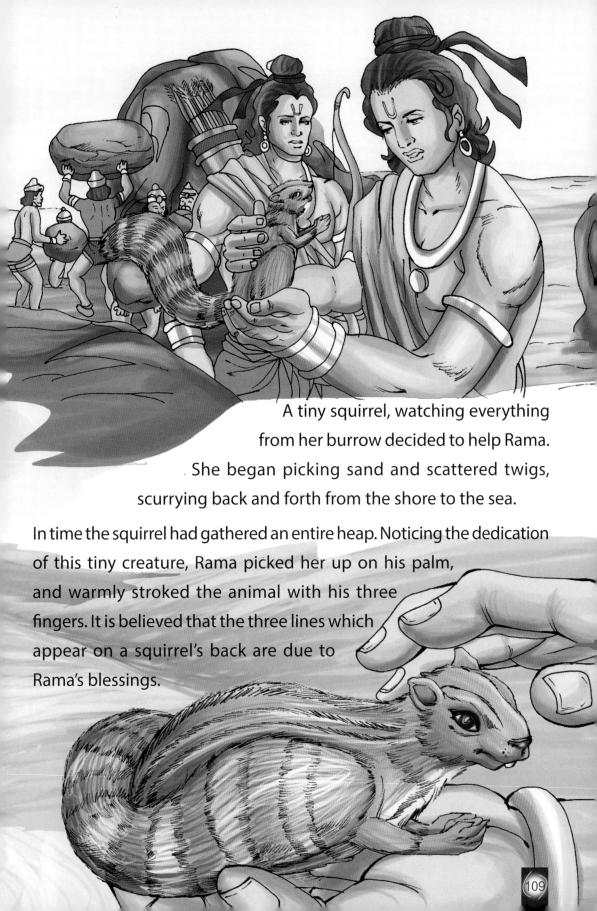

A tiny squirrel, watching everything from her burrow decided to help Rama. She began picking sand and scattered twigs, scurrying back and forth from the shore to the sea.

In time the squirrel had gathered an entire heap. Noticing the dedication of this tiny creature, Rama picked her up on his palm, and warmly stroked the animal with his three fingers. It is believed that the three lines which appear on a squirrel's back are due to Rama's blessings.

109

How the Moon Lost its Light?

King Daksha Prajapati's twenty seven daughters were married to Chandra, the Moon God, on the condition that he would treat them equally. Chandra visited the palace of one wife each night. But he loved only one of his wives, Rohini, and shone the brightest on the night when he visited her. The other wives were very sad and complained to their father, who cursed Chandra that he would stop shining.

All day Surya, the Sun God, nourished Chandra with his light. And at night Chandra produced the divine drink *soma* which nourished the Gods. But due to Daksha's curse on Chandra, the Gods lost their source of strength. They pleaded to Brahma to help. Brahma advised Chandra to chant the 'Mrityunjaya' mantra ten crore times. This pleased Lord Shiva and he partially freed him from the curse. Since then, Chandra shines only on certain nights.

The End of Kumbhakarna

When Rama spared Ravana for being unarmed, Ravana returned from the battlefield humiliated. He then decided to send his brother Kumbhakarna to fight Rama and Lakshmana.

Kumbhakarna, who was cursed to sleep for six months at a time, grew furious when awakened. Ravana explained the urgent situation to him and asked him to leave immediately.

Seeing the gigantic Kumbhakarna arrive, the monkeys started fleeing in all directions. Kumbhakarna then grabbed a handful of monkeys and ate them. Rama blocked his movements with many arrows and finally flung his *chakra* and severed the demon's head. The monkeys came back once again and rejoiced on seeing the dead body of the demon.

Sati

Brahma's son Daksha had a beautiful daughter named Sati who loved Shiva and wanted to marry him. Daksha thought he was greater than Shiva and forbade her. But Shiva and Sati married without his consent. Feeling insulted, Daksha vowed to take revenge.

Daksha arranged for a *yagna*, inviting all the Gods except Shiva. Upset by this, Sati went to meet her father at the ceremony and asked her father the reason for not inviting them. Daksha, already angry with Shiva and Sati, exploded, "Your husband is a ruffian. He is not fit to be invited," hurling insults at Shiva in front of everyone. Unable to bear this, Sati threw herself into the sacrificial fire and died.

An enraged Shiva on hearing about Sati's death, began performing the *tandav* or the dance of destruction, to destroy the entire universe.

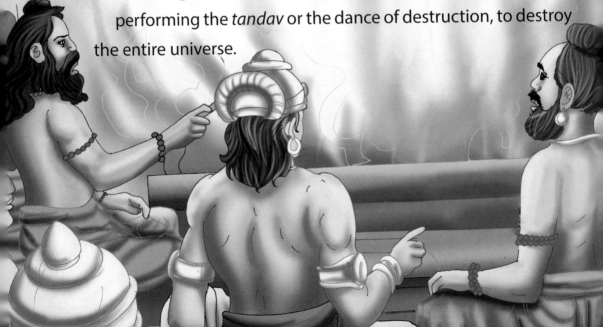

Brahma appeared and begged Shiva for forgiveness. Shiva relented but cursed Daksha to bear a goat's head forever.

Sati was later reborn as Parvati.

The Battle with Meghnad

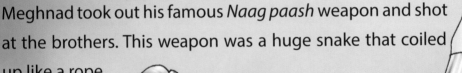

Before the final battle with Ravana, Rama and Lakshmana killed six of his demon chiefs and had begun their search for Ravana's son, Meghnad. Lord Brahma had given Meghnad the boon of invisibility. He started firing arrows at the monkey squad, who failed to discover the source of these attacks. Rama and Lakshmana understood that Meghnad was behind these invisible attacks, but before they could act, Meghnad took out his famous *Naag paash* weapon and shot at the brothers. This weapon was a huge snake that coiled up like a rope.

As Rama and Lakshmana struggled to be uncoiled, Meghnad shot several snake arrows at the brothers which pierced their bodies, making them unconscious. Thinking Rama and Lakshmana to be dead, Meghnad rushed to his father's court to give him the news.

Karna's Promise

The war between the Kauravas and Pandavas was imminent. Kunti, the Pandava's mother was disturbed by this. She went to Karna pleading, "Karna, you are actually my son. If you fight against the Pandavas, you will be fighting against your own brothers. Join the Pandavas in the war." Karna replied, "I knew that you are my real mother but you had given me up when I was only a baby; I was brought up by a charioteer. It was Duryodhana who made me the king of Anga. I am grateful to him and can't betray him. I will fight against the Pandavas."

Hearing this Kunti was upset and started weeping. Karna could not see his mother like that and declared, "I can promise you one thing. I will not harm any of the Pandavas except Arjuna who is my rival. It is Arjun alone who I will not spare. Either he would live or I would. Rest assured, you will always have five sons," Karna declared. Kunti could hardly argue further. She blessed him and left.

Krishna's Peace Mission

When Sanjay, Duryodhana's courtier failed to convince Duryodhana to compromise with the Pandavas and prevent battle, Krishna decided to go to Hastinapur as a messenger of the Pandavas and persuade Duryodhana. After receiving a warm welcome at the court, Krishna said to Duryodhana, "I come with an offer from the Pandavas. Instead of returning their whole kingdom, they would settle for just five villages as they are peace loving and want to prevent war."

Duryodhana scornfully replied, "The entire kingdom belongs to me. I will not even give land equal to the tip of a needle from my kingdom to them. You are always partial to those Pandavas. I will imprison you." He ordered his soldiers to imprison Krishna.

At that moment, Krishna worked a miracle again and suddenly he showed himself everywhere, in all things, even in the hearts of the people. Krishna actually split his image into many figures. Every corner seemed to be filled by a Krishna! Duryodhana and his soldiers desperately tried to catch the real Krishna whom they could not find! Having made his point, Krishna disappeared in a puff of air.

Lakshmana Becomes Unconscious

Meghnad, Ravana's son, was determined to kill Rama and Lakshmana. As he entered the battlefield, Lakshmana started shooting arrows at him. Soon, he destroyed Meghnad's chariot and killed his charioteer. Meghnad was furious and shot a weapon given to him by Brahma at Lakshmana. The instant the dreadful arrow hit Lakshmana, he fell unconscious. Rama rushed to his beloved brother and tried to revive him, hoping he had not died.

Bhimeshwar

Bhim was the son of the demon Kumbhakarna. Bhim performed *tapasya* for one year and pleased Brahma who gave him many boons. He captured heaven and earth, banning all kinds of worship on earth. Those who tried to worship Gods were imprisoned. He also imprisoned Shiva's devotee Sudakshina. All the Gods pleaded Shiva to kill Bhim. One day, Sudakshina made a *Shivalinga* in the prison and started worshipping it. When Bhim came to know about this, he went to the prison and struck the *Shivalinga* with a sword. Out came Shiva himself and burnt Bhim with one blow of his breath. The *Shivalinga* was called Bhimeshwar and is still worshipped.

Bhishma Falls

During the Mahabharata, fierce fighting ensued for nine days. On the tenth day, Arjuna and Bhishma were face–to–face. Arjuna showered arrows on Bhishma, which pierced every inch of his body. Bhishma fell on the ground, his body supported by a bed of arrows with his head hanging down. Arjuna shot three arrows to support Bhishma's hanging head. "I am thirsty," said the dying Bhishma to Arjuna who shot an arrow to the ground and a fountain of water gushed out of it, reaching Bhishma's mouth. Bhishma blessed Arjuna and called Duryodhana warning him for the last time to come to a settlement with the Pandavas. Karna then came to pay homage to Bhishma and begged pardon for his past misconduct. The fall of Bhishma marked the beginning of the defeat of the Kauravas.

The End of Meghnad

After a terrible encounter, Ravana realized that Rama and Lakshmana were still alive. He once again sent for Meghnad, who attacked veiled in smoke from his flying chariot. Hundreds of monkeys died on the spot.

Meghnad then using his illusory powers, created a hallucination of Sita and holding her by her hair, paraded her around in his chariot and finally cut off her head. Rama was devastated by this news, but was assured by Vibhishana that this was one of Meghnad's tricks as he needed time to perform a *yagna* which would bring him invincibility on its completion. Lakshmana climbing on Hanuman's shoulders, found Meghnad and launching the *Indraastra* killed him.

The Broken Code of War

During the battle, Drona, the royal guru to the Kauravas was ordered to capture Yudhisthira alive, so Arjuna always protected him. Once Arjuna fighting some Kaurava warriors left Yudhisthira unprotected. Drona and his soldiers approached Yudhisthira forming a circular military formation known as *chakravyuh* around him. Arjuna's son, Abhimanyu, had learned how to enter the *chakravyuh* from his father but did not know how to come out.

Only Arjuna knew how to break the *chakravyuh*. Nevertheless, Abhimanyu decided to enter the formation.

Jaidhratha, the king of Sindhudesha, who had obtained a boon from Shiva that he would be able to stop the Pandavas for one day, stopped them from entering the *chakravyuh* to help Abhimanyu. Six warriors including Drona, Duryodhana, and Karna together attacked Abhimanyu who eventually lost all his weapons. Finally, the Kaurava warriors broke the code of war; and attacking the unarmed Abhimanyu, killed him.

The End of Jaidratha

Arjuna came to know that his son, Abhimanyu, had been killed against the code of war and that Jaidratha was responsible for it. Grief–stricken and furious, he took a vow. "Either I will end Jaidratha's life before the sun sets on the fourteenth day or I will kill myself." On the fourteenth day, the Kaurava army was arranged to give Jaidratha protection. But Arjuna cut through the array of soldiers and reached Jaidratha. And just as he was going to kill him, there was darkness.

The Kauravas were happy that the sun had set and Arjuna would now
have to kill himself. Arjuna was sad but Krishna told him, "The sun has
not yet set. I have covered the sun by my *Sudershan Chakra* (discus).
Now is the moment; Jaidratha is looking at the horizon. Kill him!"
The next moment, the sun emerged and an arrow from Arjuna's bow
struck Jaidratha dead.

The Fall of Drona

As the fourteenth day of the battle of Kurukshetra drew to a close, Drona was unhappy as he was unable to capture Yudhisthira and could not even save Jaidratha. So he attacked the Pandava soldiers with even more vigour. Krishna told the Pandavas that Drona could be killed by a trick. He asked the Pandavas to spread the false news of Drona's son, Ashwatthama, being killed.

Bhima killed an elephant named Ashvatthama and shouted, "I have killed Ashvatthama." When Drona heard this, he was full of sorrow. He asked Yudhisthira whether it was true, knowing that Yudhisthira would never lie. Yudhisthira replied, "Yes, Ashvatthama is dead, but the elephant not your son." However Krishna asked the drummers to beat the drums when Yudhisthira spoke the last part of the sentence, so Drona couldn't hear it. As Drona sat mourning his son's death, Dhrishtadyumna who had been born to kill Drona, cut his head off.

Karna Meets His End

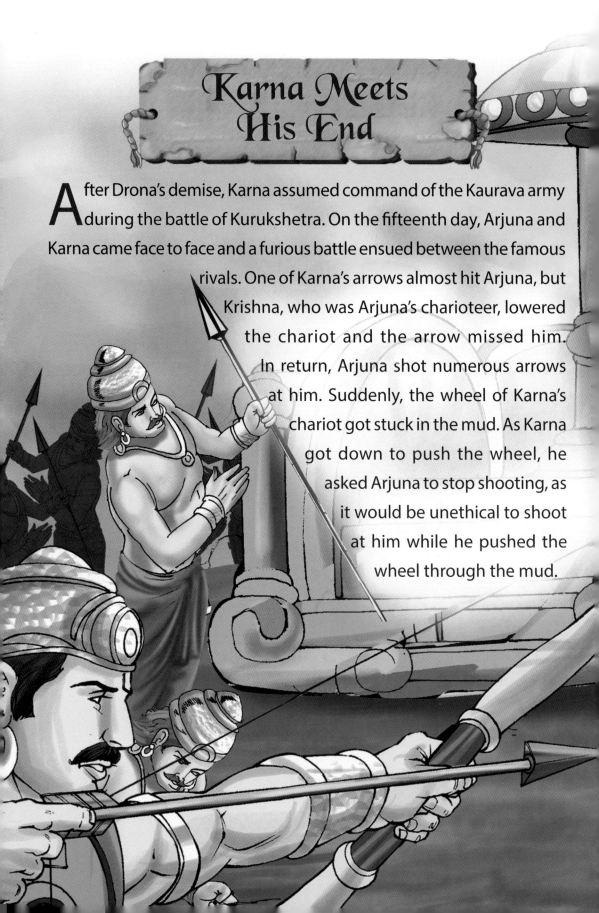

After Drona's demise, Karna assumed command of the Kaurava army during the battle of Kurukshetra. On the fifteenth day, Arjuna and Karna came face to face and a furious battle ensued between the famous rivals. One of Karna's arrows almost hit Arjuna, but Krishna, who was Arjuna's charioteer, lowered the chariot and the arrow missed him. In return, Arjuna shot numerous arrows at him. Suddenly, the wheel of Karna's chariot got stuck in the mud. As Karna got down to push the wheel, he asked Arjuna to stop shooting, as it would be unethical to shoot at him while he pushed the wheel through the mud.

Krishna retorted, "You shot at the unarmed Abhimanyu. Was that fair?" Arjuna was reminded by Krishna about the instance when the Kauravas broke the code of war and killed Abhimanyu mercilessly. He told Arjuna to do his duty. Hearing this, Arjuna filled with righteous anger, killed Karna.

Gandhari Tries to Protect Her Son

Gandhari was worried about Duryodhana as he was her only son who was alive. With a plan in mind to secure his safety, she asked him to take a bath and appear naked in front of her. She would open the cloth over her eyes and cast a look on his body. By the mystic power of her eyes she planned to make his body invincible. Krishna came to know of her plan.

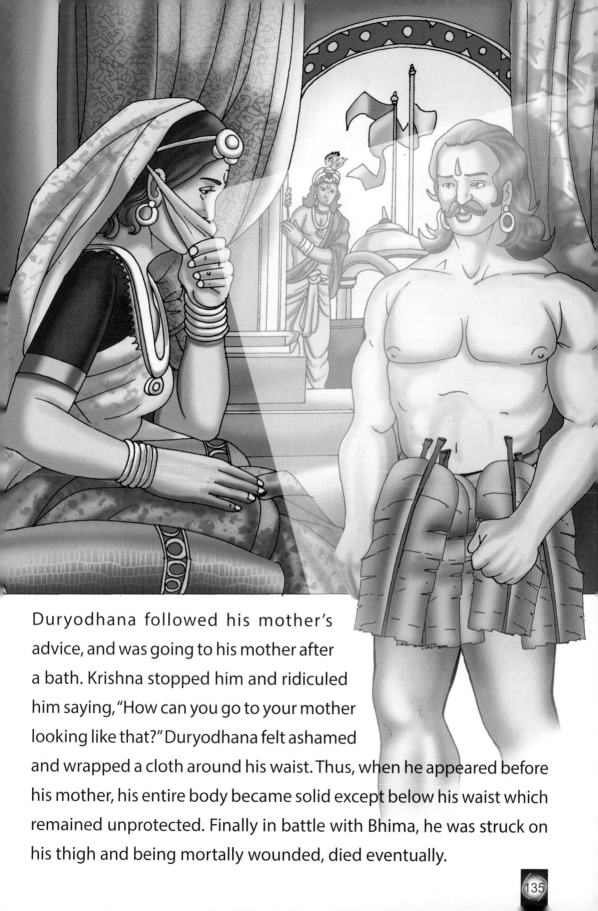

Duryodhana followed his mother's advice, and was going to his mother after a bath. Krishna stopped him and ridiculed him saying, "How can you go to your mother looking like that?" Duryodhana felt ashamed and wrapped a cloth around his waist. Thus, when he appeared before his mother, his entire body became solid except below his waist which remained unprotected. Finally in battle with Bhima, he was struck on his thigh and being mortally wounded, died eventually.

The True Devotee

Hanuman, a loyal follower of Rama, worshipped him sincerely. One day, Sita gave him a precious pearl necklace. Hanuman immediately broke the necklace and started looking at each pearl carefully. He glared at each pearl and threw them away, one by one, in disgust. Surprised, Sita asked him for an explanation.

Hanuman explained, "I am looking for Lord Rama's image in the pearls." Hanuman believed that Rama was present everywhere and was disappointed that his image was not in the pearls. He declared the pearls were just stones and pebbles and therefore worthless. When the people around him asked if Rama was present in Hanuman, Hanuman tore open his chest with his hands and everyone was amazed to see a brilliant image of Rama and Sita engraved in his heart.

The people accepted Hanuman to be a true devotee of Rama. He is therefore also known as Bhakta Hanuman.

Ashvatthama's Plan

When Dronacharya's son, Ashvatthama, found out that Duryodhana was dying, he was furious and vowed to kill the Pandavas. Devising an evil plan, Ashvatthama took two warriors and went to the Pandavas' army camp at night. First, he went to Draupadi's brother, Dhrishtadyumna and strangled him while he was asleep. Then, one by one, he killed all the five sons of Draupadi and finally, Shikhandi, Draupadi's elder brother. The Pandavas and Draupadi were not in the camp at that time. Eventually, setting fire to the camp, he quickly fled. Next morning, the Pandavas were shocked to see what had happened. Draupadi was devastated. Meanwhile, Ashvatthama rushed to Duryodhana to inform him of his success. Pleased, Duryodhana breathed his last.

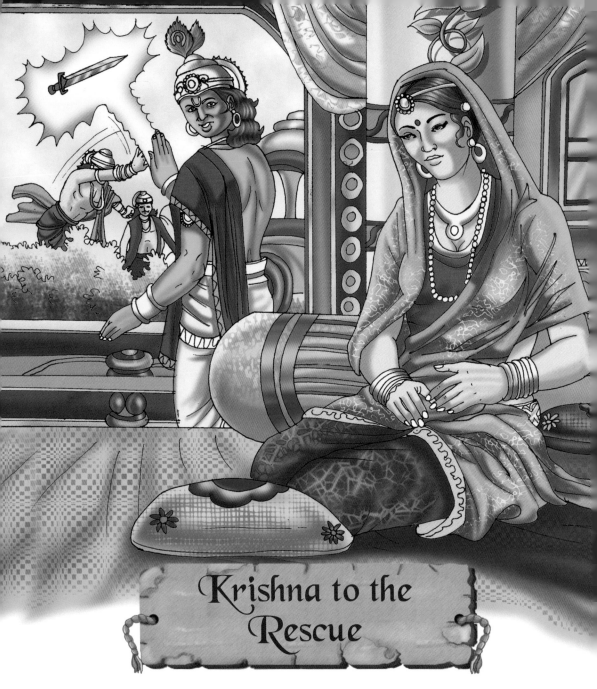

Krishna to the Rescue

The Pandavas were enraged with Ashvatthama, Dronacharya's son, for setting their camp on fire. When Ashvatthama saw the Pandavas approaching, he picked up a blade of grass and ordered, "May this destroy the race of the Pandavas." The blade went towards the womb of Uttara, Abhimanyu's wife. As it took the form of a dagger, Krishna diffused its power. Thus he saved Uttara and her child.

Sita's Exile

Rama, a fair and just king was admired by his kingdom for his wisdom and strength. One day, one of his spies told him that the people of Ayodhya were unhappy because they believed that he should not have accepted Sita after Ravana had kidnapped her. Disheartened, Rama decided to send Sita away in order to keep his people happy.

Rama instructed Lakshmana, "Take Sita and leave her on the banks of the river Ganga near Sage Valmiki's ashram." Lakshmana was astonished at the request but could not disobey Rama. Next morning, Lakshmana took Sita along with him to the river and told her that Rama had asked him to leave her there. Sita was shocked. How could Rama doubt her? But then being a devoted wife, she did not oppose him. She remained under Sage Valmiki's care while Lakshmana returned with a heavy heart to Ayodhya.

Sahasramukharavana

Sahasramukharavana was Ravana's son. He was but a child when his father was killed by Rama. To avenge his father's death, he decided to attack Rama's kingdom.

Sahasramukharavana had obtained a boon from Brahma that none but a truly chaste (pure character) woman would be able to harm him. Protected by this boon, the hundred headed demon entered Kosala, determined to destroy Ayodhya. Neither Rama nor his armies could stop his advance. Then, learning about the boon from Brahma, the women of Ayodhya were asked to enter the battlefield. But alas, not one woman was chaste enough to defeat the dreaded demon.

Rama realized that only one woman could save his city and that was his wife, Sita. But Rama knew that Sita would not come voluntarily to the city that had rejected her.

Thus, Rama sent a message to Sita saying that he was dying. On hearing this, Sita rushed to Ayodhya to catch a glimpse of her husband before he passed away. On the outskirts of the city, the rakshasa Sahasramukharavana blocked her path and refused to let her pass. Outraged by Sahasramukharavana's action, impatient to meet her dying husband, Sita picked up a blade of grass, transformed it into the lethal Shaktika missile with the power of her chastity and hurled it at the rakshasa. The missile ripped through Sahasramukharavana's heart and killed him instantly.

Yamaraj Meets Rama

Having ruled Ayodhya for ages, Rama grew tired and wanted to go to heaven. Realizing this, Vishnu asked Yamaraj to bring Rama back. Yamaraj disguising himself as a sage went to Ayodhya. Meeting Lakshmana at the entrance, Yamraj told him that they were not to be disturbed.

Ushered in, Yamaraj ordered Rama to kill anyone who would disturb them and finally said, "I have come to take you to heaven."

Meanwhile, an ill tempered Sage Durvasa arrived at the palace, ordering Lakshmana to allow him to meet Rama. Lakshmana refused. Enraged, Durvasa cursed Lakshmana to leave the earth and go to heaven. But when, Durvasa saw Rama with Yamaraj, he realized his mistake. Meanwhile, Lakshmana, being cursed to die, walked towards the river Sarayu and held his breath till he died. Grief stricken by his brother's death, Rama too went to the river Sarayu and walked into it.

Kartikeya

Once, a demon called Taraka performed a long and difficult *tapasya*. Pleased with him, Brahma granted him the boon that only a son of Shiva could kill him.

With this boon, Taraka became proud and selfish and created havoc on earth. Seeing the chaos, the devastated Gods requested Shiva to stop Taraka. At that time, Shiva did not have any sons. To create a son, Shiva took a form with six faces with each having a third eye. Six sparks burst from these eyes and formed six babies.

Parvati, Shiva's wife was elated and took all the babies in her arms to embrace them. But her embrace was so tight, that the six babies turned into one baby with six heads.

This baby called Kartikeya grew to be a strong boy who went with an army of Gods to battle Taraka and killed him. Since then, Kartikeya is known as the God of war.

Lord Buddha

Buddha, meaning 'the enlightened one,' was born in the ancient city of Kapilavastu, to King Sudhodana and Queen Maya. An avatar of Vishnu, the young prince, named Siddhartha, was not attracted to the luxurious life of the palace. Instead he grew sad seeing the misery of the common man.

Seeing his son lose interest in worldly matters, Sudhodana married Siddhartha to a young woman. Though they had a son and Siddhartha continued living in the palace, he remained unhappy. One day, he left his family and the palace behind to lead a hermit's life in the forests.

Under the bodhi tree in Gaya, he achieved *nirvana* or eternal peace. He travelled all over India spreading his message. He founded the religion of *Buddhism*, which is based on his teachings.

Yama Kumar

Once Yama, the God of death, married a woman from earth and started living there. They had a son called Yama Kumar. Yama soon realized his wife's cunning nature. She always quarrelled with him, so he went back to his kingdom. His wife did not teach Yama Kumar anything so when he grew up he was incapable of earning a living.

One day, Yama appeared before his son and said, "You should learn about medicine."

Soon Yama Kumar became a doctor. Yama declared, "Whenever you see me near a patient, it means that the patient is going to die. You must refuse to treat that patient." So, Yama Kumar treated only those who were going to survive. Thus, he became famous.

One day the princess fell ill. Many doctors from far and wide tried to cure her, but failed. So, Yama Kumar went to see her. Seeing his father there, he realized that the princess's death was inevitable.

He then pleaded, "Father, please do not take the princess, she is so young and beautiful."

Yama replied, "I have to fulfil my duty, but for your sake I will take her after three days."

Yama Kumar devised a plan to save the princess. When Yama returned, he shouted, "Mother! Father is here, you can meet him." Not wanting to see his wife, the petrified Yama ran away without taking the princess.

Since Yama Kumar saved the princess's life, the joyous king married his daughter to Yama Kumar.

Brahma Tests Krishna

Amazed to see little Krishna perform wonderful feats, Brahma devised a plan to test him.

One day, while Krishna was out with his friends tending the cattle, he saw them all disappearing one by one. Seeing his friends disappear, Krishna was surprised. He immediately understood that this was the doing of Lord Brahma. Not wanting to return without his friends and cattle as it would make their parents anxious, he tried to convince Brahma of his ability.

Krishna started assuming various forms. As he was God himself, Krishna could take on any form he desired. In a while the entire field was again crowded with all his friends. The calves too appeared some mooing and some grazing the fields. It looked exactly like before.

Startled, Brahma realized Krishna's immense powers and showered flowers from the heavens above.

Satyavan and Savitri

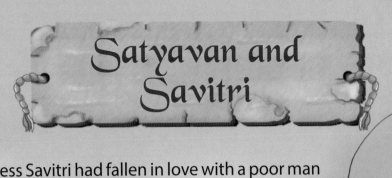

Princess Savitri had fallen in love with a poor man called Satyavan. Narada Muni warned her not to marry Satyavan as he would die at an early age. Unmoved, Savitri married Satyavan.

On the day of Satyavan's death, she saw that Yama himself had come to take him. She begged Yama not to take Satyavan. But Yama said that no one could stop death. Savitri followed them for miles and miles. Impressed with her determination, Yama said, "I will give you two boons. You can ask for anything except Satyavan's life."

For the first boon, Savitri asked for the well being of her father-in-law.

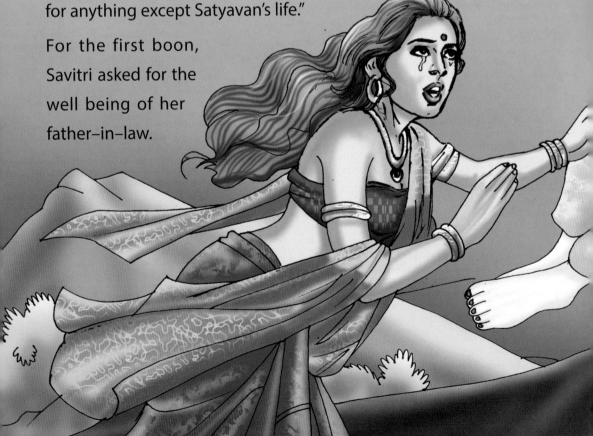

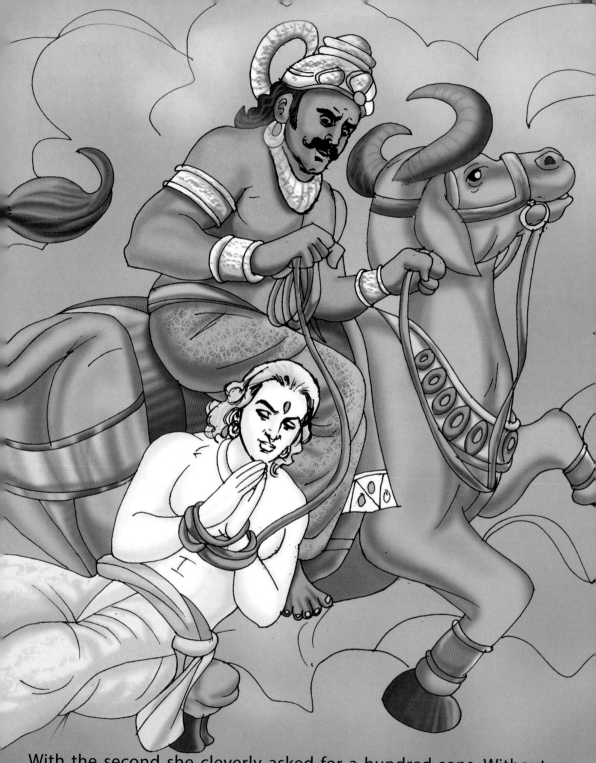

With the second she cleverly asked for a hundred sons. Without thinking, Yama granted her the two boons. At this Savitri asked Yama to return her husband because without him, she could not have any sons. Defeated, Yama returned Savitri her husband.

How Kali was Created?

Engaged in battle, Durga realized that she would have to change herself into a violent and destructive force in order to kill the demons Chandra and Mundra.

In a fit of rage, Durga poured out lightening from her third eye. From this stark light a dark female figure (Kali) emerged, with blazing eyes and dishevelled hair, her red tongue shining bright. She did not wear diamonds or gold, rather a garland of human skulls, and cobras as bracelets. Armed with a trident, a sword, and a human skull in three hands respectively, she gave her blessings with her fourth hand. Kali is the fierce form of Durga or Parvati.

Once created, the blood–thirsty Goddess went on killing the demons. She killed Chandra and Mundra and earned the name of 'Chamundra.' Even when all the demons were killed, Kali did not stop her murderous rampage! The dance of death ensued. In order to stop her rampage, Shiva appeared and threw himself at her feet. Seeing Shiva at her feet, she realized her mistake and stopped the slaughter.

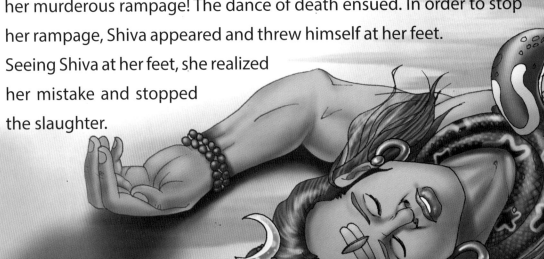

Krishna, the Shepherd Boy

As children, Krishna and his brother Balaram helped their father look after their cattle. They often grazed the cattle in the pastures of Gokul.

While the cattle grazed, Krishna played melodious tunes on his flute or enjoyed games with his friends.

One day while he and his friends were playing in the fields, Krishna noticed a new cow in his herd. Alarmed, he called Balaram. Krishna told him that the cow looked different and did not belong to them. Balaram agreed with Krishna.

Quietly, the brothers approached the cow. Krishna held the cow by its tail and whirled it around, finally throwing it on the ground. Just as the cow fell, it transformed into a monster and died. Krishna told his friends that the monster had taken the form of a cow to kill him.

His friends rejoiced at the death of the monster and congratulated Krishna for his courage and strength.

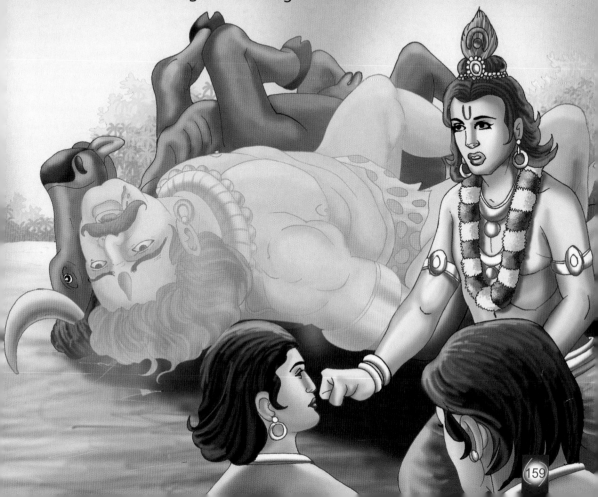

Sage Agastya and the Demons

Ivala and Vatapi were two demon brothers who hated and tormented all Brahmins. The first demon could take any form, and the second knew the secret of bringing the dead to life.

One day, they decided to kill the great Sage Agastya. They planned that Ilvala would turn into a goat and Vatapi would kill it and offer it to Agastya.

Then using his powers he would bring him back to life. Ilvala would tear Agastya's stomach to come out, killing Agastya. Sage Agastya came to know of the wicked plan and decided to teach the two brothers a lesson. When Vatapi invited him to eat the meat, Agastya ate the goat meat, but before the demon could bring his brother back to life, he digested the meat, killing Ilvala. Enraged, Vatapi rushed towards the Sage, baring his teeth. Agastya merely opened his eyes, and there lay in front of him, a heap of ashes.

Valmiki

There was once a robber who looted travellers. One day, he tried to loot a traveller who had nothing. The traveller said, "I am Narada. Why do you commit the sin of robbing people?" The robber replied, "I have to support my family."

Narada said, "Go and ask your family if they would share your sin like they share your loot."

The robber went and asked his father, "I bring money by robbing people. Will you share my guilt?" Furious, his father shouted, "Get lost, you robber!" His mother too was enraged and said, "Why should I? I never stole a thing in my life." His wife stated, "It is your duty to support me." He then returned to Narada who said, "Everybody is alone in this world. Worship God, it is he who stands by you always." The robber prayed for many years. Then he heard a voice from heaven, "Your new name is Valmiki and you will write the story of Rama." Valmiki wrote the *Ramayana*.

Krishna Kills Aghasura

The Gods were anxiously waiting for someone powerful to kill the deadly demon, Aghasura.

Aghasura wanted to avenge the killing of his siblings, Putana and Bakasura, by Krishna. Deciding to use his great mystic powers, he changed himself into a gigantic black serpent and arrived before Krishna and his friends.

Seeing the enormous creature which had fiery eyes and was breathing hotly, the boys grew curious. Its mouth expanded from the skies to the land. Wanting to probe further, the boys entered its mouth. But Aghasura was waiting for Krishna. Finally, Krishna stepped in and Aghasura snapped his jaws so hard that it nearly crushed the boys. Using his powers, Krishna enlarged himself to such a huge size that the python could not close its mouth and devour all of them.

Aghasura now found it difficult to even breathe. Soon, he was chocked to death and Krishna and his friends came out safe and sound.

The Forest Fire

After slaying the great Serpent Kaliya, Krishna and his people were passing a forest on their way home. As night fell, it became impossible to proceed. So they decided to spend the night in the forest. Soon, a great forest fire erupted, spreading wildly. It began scorching the entire forest. Scared, the people ran to Krishna to save them from the raging fire. They knew that only Krishna, who possessed great powers, could save them.

Krishna looked at the fire blazing in the distance and stood firm. As it came close, he opened his mouth wide, swallowing the destructive forest fire. Amazed by his strength, the people rejoiced and hailed the Lord with praise.

The Reformation of Duraasadana

When the demon Bhasmasura was killed by Vishnu, his son Duraasadana was enraged. He performed a long *tapasya*, obtaining the boon of immortality from Shiva. Terrified, the Gods left heaven and hid in Kashi. Duraasadana followed them and so they escaped to Kedarnath. There, the Gods prayed to Parvati. An avatar of Ganesha, Vakratunda, with five faces and ten hands came out of Parvati's face. She gave him a lion to ride. Vakratunda went and fought with Duraasadana. Assuming his huge form (*vishvaroop*), Vakratunda placed his foot on Duraasadana's head to remove all his evil thoughts.

Duraasadana was reformed and Vakratunda gave him the duty of removing evil, henceforth.

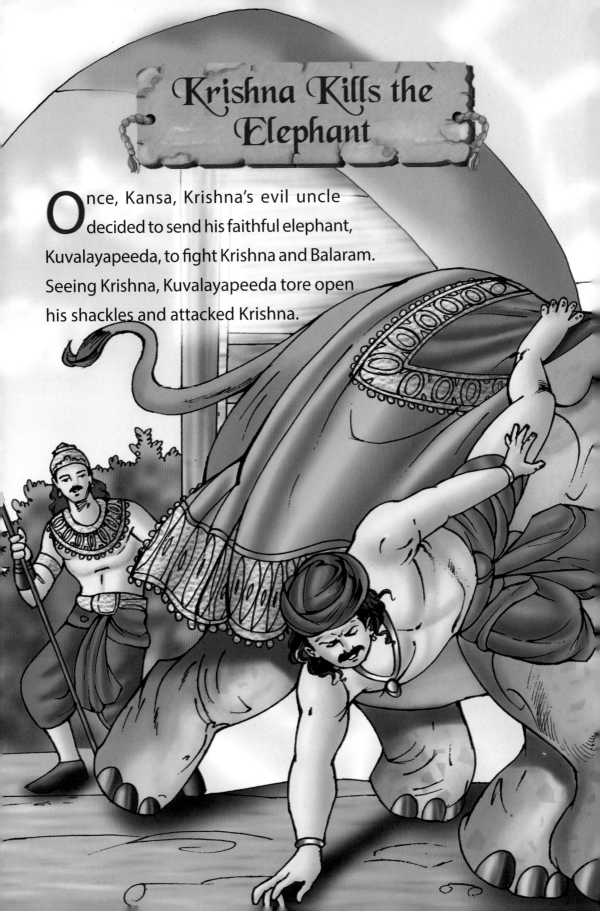

Krishna Kills the Elephant

Once, Kansa, Krishna's evil uncle decided to send his faithful elephant, Kuvalayapeeda, to fight Krishna and Balaram. Seeing Krishna, Kuvalayapeeda tore open his shackles and attacked Krishna.

Charging towards him, the elephant grabbed Krishna with his trunk, and was about to throw him on the ground when Krishna slipped out of his grip and quickly hid behind his hind legs. Seeing Krishna slip out, Kuvalayapeeda raised his leg to crush him, but he again escaped unhurt. Seeing the ferocious elephant–demon, Balaram rushed to save his brother. Casting a cruel glance at the brothers, the elephant charged towards them with his huge tusks. Krishna and Balaram firmly grabbed each of his tusks and broke them. As the elephant fell on the ground, the brothers killed him with his own tusks.

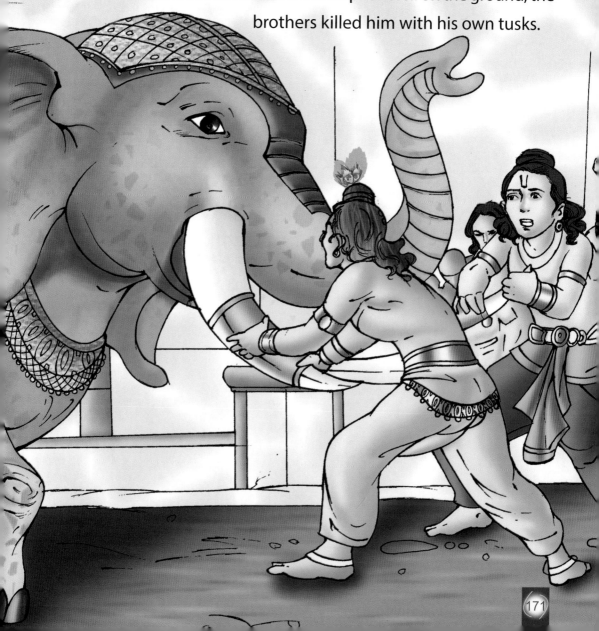

Indra's Weapon

Once, Vritrasur, a powerful demon, decided to conquer heaven. He fought with the Gods and swallowed all their weapons. The Gods pleaded to Vishnu for help. "Through his long penance, the bones of Sage Dhadichi have become very strong. Only a weapon made of his bones can kill Vritrasur. But beware! You can't kill Dhadichi, as he is my devotee. You have to request him to sacrifice his life," revealed Vishnu.

The Gods, led by Indra, went to Dhadichi and begged for his bones. Dhadichi agreed to sacrifice his life, but he wanted to go on a pilgrimage before that. Hearing this, Indra brought all the holy places near him. After taking dips in the holy waters, Dhadichi gave up his life. Indra thus made a weapon called Vajra from his bones and killed Vritrasur.

Kedarnath

According to legend, the Pandavas having won the Mahabharata war went on a pilgrimage to Mount Kailash to be cleansed by Lord Shiva for their sins of killing countless people. Seeing them approach, Shiva hid. When they couldn't find him, Yudhisthira said, "I know you have hidden because we have sinned, but we will not leave without seeing you." As they moved ahead, a bull attacked them. Bhima started fighting it. The bull hid his head within a crack in a rock. Bhima tried to pull him out by his tail, but the body of the bull got separated from his head.

The body turned into a *Shivalinga* from which appeared Shiva, who forgave them for their sins.

The *linga* is still present in the Himalayas and is called *Kedarnath*.

The Demon with Thousand Hands

Once a demon named Banasura had a thousand hands with which he played the *mridanga*, while Shiva danced the *tandav*. Pleased with his talent, Shiva became his protector. Soon, Banasura became very arrogant and powerful. Banasura had a daughter named Usha. One day, she saw a man in her dream and fell in love with him. Usha's friend, Chitralekha, painted a picture of the man in the dream based on Usha's description. The picture resembled Anniruddha, Krishna's grandson. Usha asked her friend to help her meet Anniruddha. Chitralekha went to Anniruddha and brought him to Usha.

They fell in love with each other. Banasura disapproved of this and imprisoned Anniruddha. Hearing this, Krishna came to rescue of his grandson and fought Banasura. In the end Krishna defeated Banasura. Finally, at Shiva's request, Krishna spared Banasura's life but cut off his thousand hands leaving only four.

Luv & Kush Fight Lakshman

After defeating Shatrughana's army, Luv and Kush did not return the sacred horse. Hearing the news, Rama sent Lakshmana to Valmiki's ashram to bring back the horse which he needed for a *yagna*. However, the stubborn brothers, Luv and Kush refused to part with the horse without a fight. Under Valmiki's guidance, Luv and Kush had gained expertise in archery and were not afraid of Lakshmana.

A fight ensued between them and Lakshmana. Kush promptly took his bow and arrow and sent an arrow flying towards Lakshmana. Furious, Lakshmana began to retaliate. Lakshmana was very impressed with the strength and might of the two brothers. Luv and Kush shot many arrows at Lakshmana and finally Lakshmana fell to the ground, defeated.

Curse on Parikshit

Abhimanyu's son, Parikshit became the King of Hastinapur after the Pandavas left for the mountains.

One day, while wandering in the forest, Parikshit felt thirsty. Seeing a sage, he asked him for some water.

The meditating sage did not hear Parikshit. Losing his temper, the King lifted a dead snake and put it on the shoulders of the sage like a garland. Just then, the sage's son returned and saw Parikshit do this.

Furious, he cursed Parikshit to die from a snakebite within seven days. The sage scolded his son and sent a message to the King informing him about the curse. Soon, a big palace was built, where Parikshit could be safe from snakes. However, on the seventh day, the King of serpents, Takshaka, disguised himself as a worm and entered a fruit. The moment the king bit the fruit, Takshaka assumed his real form and coiled himself around Parikshit, killing him.

The Snake Sacrifice

After Parikshit's death, his son Janmejaya was crowned the king of Hastinapur. Wanting to avenge his father's death, Janmejaya resolved to kill Takshaka.

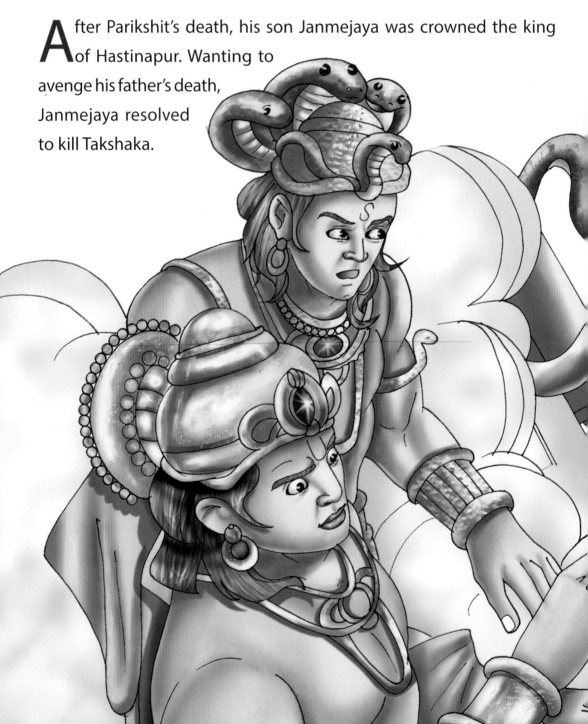

He decided to organize a snake sacrifice. Accordingly, a sacrificial fire was burnt where the holy priests chanted the names of different snakes.

As a result, the snakes became powerless and fell into the sacrificial fire one by one and perished. The great snake sacrifice continued for many days and hundreds and thousands of snakes emerged from everywhere and surrendered to the fire. Everyone waited for Takshaka but he was missing. Everyone, including the priests and Jamnejaya were puzzled. They never knew that Takshaka had fled to Indra for protection.

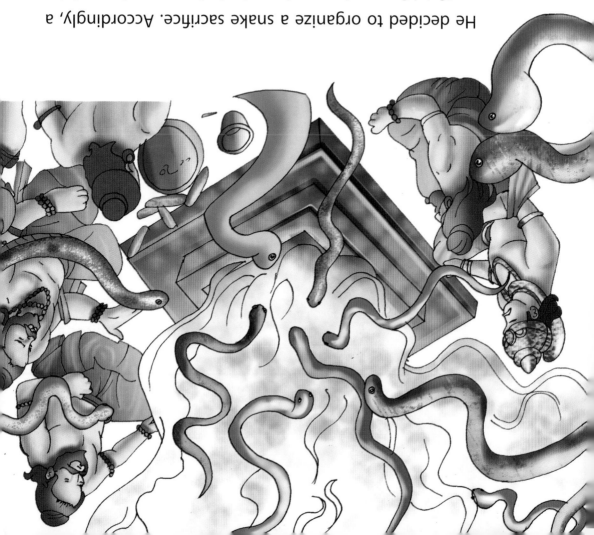

Astika Saves Takshaka

Janmejaya held a snake sacrifice to avenge his father's death at the hands of Takshaka. Mantras were chanted to destroy the snakes but Takshaka did not appear. The head priests thought that Takshaka had sought protection from Indra. They chanted a special mantra to compel Takshaka to materialize and fall in the sacrificial fire along with Indra.